# Silver Burdett Ginn Science
# DISCOVERYWORKS

## Welcome

to Silver Burdett Ginn **Science DiscoveryWorks** – a science program that engages students in active investigations of scientific concepts. **Science DiscoveryWorks** reflects our belief that the best science education for students is one that gradually introduces them to the knowledge, methods, skills, and attitudes of scientists, while simultaneously recognizing and respecting the educational and developmental needs of all students.`

**Silver Burdett Ginn**
**Parsippany, NJ     Needham, MA**
**Atlanta, GA     Irving, TX     Deerfield, IL     Santa Clara, CA**

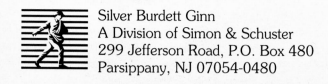

Silver Burdett Ginn
A Division of Simon & Schuster
299 Jefferson Road, P.O. Box 480
Parsippany, NJ 07054-0480

Acknowledgements appear on pages A66, B82, C66, D82, E82, and F66, which constitute extensions of this copyright page.

**Grade 3 Unified Teaching Guide**       ISBN 0-382-31982-6

**Modular Teaching Guides**
Unit A: Life Cycles                  ISBN 0-382-33462-0
Unit B: Sun, Moon, and Earth         ISBN 0-382-33463-9
Unit C: Forms of Energy              ISBN 0-382-33464-7
Unit D: Earth's Water                ISBN 0-382-33465-5
Unit E: Roles of Living Things       ISBN 0-382-33466-3
Unit F: What's for Lunch?            ISBN 0-382-33467-1

4 5 6 7 8 9 10  W 05 04 03 02 01 00 99 98 97

## Teacher Reviewers

**Lisa Acy**
Louis Agassiz Elementary Sch.
Cleveland, OH

**Judith Ball**
Coordinator for
Math/Science/Health
School District U46
Elgin, IL

**Karen R. Bishop**
Ferron Elementary School
Ferron, UT

**Jean Blackshear**
Fred A. Toomer Elementary Sch.
Atlanta, GA

**Bonnie Bohrer**
Brookview Elementary School
Brook Park, OH

**Robert L. Burtch**
1990 Presidential Award Winner
Batavia Middle School
Batavia, IL

**Martha Christine**
Calypso Elementary School
Bethlehem, PA

**Mary Eve Corrigan**
The Columbus Academy
Gahanna, OH

**John S. Detrick**
Emeritus Dept. Chair of
Mathematics and Holder of the
McElroy Chair of Mathematics
The Columbus Academy
Gahanna, OH

**Robert C. Dixon**
National Center to Improve the
Tools of Educators (NCITE)
University of Oregon, College
of Education
Eugene, OR

**Denise Pitts-Downing**
James Elverson Middle School
Philadelphia, PA

**Michaeline A. Dudas**
Science and Math Instructional
Support/Consultant
Northbrook, IL

**William Dudrow**
The Columbus Academy
Gahanna, OH

**Barbara Elliott**
1990 Presidential Award Winner
Ray E. Kilmer Elementary School
Colorado Springs, CO

**Fred Fabry**
Retired teacher of Geology
and Biology
Deerfield High School
Deerfield, IL

**Rhea Foster**
Anderson Park Elementary Sch.
Atlanta, GA

**Linda Froschauer**
1993 Presidential Award Winner
Weston Middle School
Weston, CT

**Joanne Gallagher**
Tamarac Middle School
Melrose, NY

**Marlene Gregor**
Elem. Science Consultant
Bloomington, IL

**William L. Handy, Jr.**
Parkland School District
Orefield, PA

**Beverly Hanrahan**
Franconia Elementary School
Souderton, PA

**Renee Harris**
Northwestern Lehigh Mid. Sch.
New Tripoli, PA

**Rhonda Hicks**
James Elverson Middle School
Philadelphia, PA

**Sr. Marie Patrice Hoare, S.L.**
Loretto Middle School
El Paso, TX

**Lester Y. Ichinose, Ph.D.**
Evanston, IL

**Mace A. Ishida, Ph.D.**
Diversity and Ed. Consultant
Blacklick, OH

**Kristine D. Jackson**
Belleville, IL

**Pearline A. James**
W. F. Slaton Elementary School
Atlanta, GA

**Evette Jones**
Grover Cleveland Elementary
Philadelphia, PA

**Charlene Kalinski**
L. L. Hotchkiss Elementary Sch.
Dallas, TX

**Sr. Sharon Kassing, S.L.**
St. Pius Catholic School
Kirkwood, MO

**John Kibler**
InterAmerica Intercultural
Training Institute
Des Plaines, IL

**Sharon Lempner**
R. G. Jones School
Cleveland, OH

**Barbara Leonard**
1992 Presidential Award Winner
Heritage Elementary School
Pueblo, CO

**Gus Liss**
Young Elementary School
Burlington Township, NJ

**Jo Ann Liss**
Intervale School
Parsippany, NJ

**Marlenn Maicki**
1990 Presidential Award Winner
Detroit Country Day School
Bloomfield Hills, MI

**Lynn Malok**
Spring Garden Elementary Sch.
Bethlehem, PA

**Barbara Mecker**
Rockwood South Middle Sch.
St. Louis, MO

**Leonardo Melton**
Fred A. Toomer Elementary Sch.
Atlanta, GA

**Bonnie Meyer**
Tremont Elementary School
Cleveland, OH

**Dr. Suzanne Moore**
L. L. Hotchkiss Elementary Sch.
Dallas, TX

**Kathy Morton**
Christ the King School
Atlanta, GA

**Dr. Ngoc-Diep T. Nguyen**
Director, Bilingual and
Multicultural Program
Schaumburg, IL

**Michael O'Shea**
R. G. Jones School
Cleveland, OH

**Wendy Peterson**
Harvey Rice Elementary School
Cleveland, OH

**Alexandra Pond**
Science Coordinator
North Shore School
Chicago, IL

**Erika Silverman**
Public School 41
Bronx, NY

**Christine Spinner**
Parma, OH

**Jean Ann Strillacci**
Kennedy Elementary School
Succasunna, NJ

**Laura Swanson**
WATTS Intermediate School
Burlington City, NJ

**Arthur F. Tobia**
Public School 41
Bronx, NY

**Nancy Vibeto**
1993 Presidential Award Winner
Jim Hill Middle School
Minot, ND

**Sandra Wilson**
McKinley Elementary School
Abington, PA

**Bonita Wylie**
Excelsior Middle School
Shorewood, MN

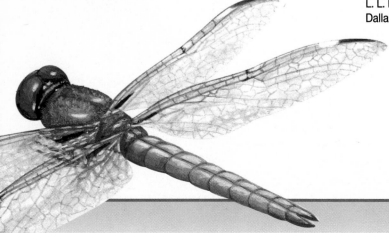

# THE SCOPE OF THE PROGRAM
## An Overview of Concepts and Themes

| | KINDERGARTEN | GRADE 1 | GRADE 2 |
|---|---|---|---|
| **Life Science**  | **UNIT A Characteristics of Living Things** <br> Classification of objects as living or nonliving; basic needs and stages of growth of living things <br> **Themes:** *Systems, Constancy and Change* | **UNIT A Kinds of Living Things** <br> The similarities and differences between plants and animals; classifying plants and animals according to one characteristic <br> **Theme:** *Systems* | **UNIT A Interactions of Living Things** <br> The needs of living things; plant and animal adaptations to various habitats; the effect of living things, including people, and natural forces on environments <br> **Themes:** *Constancy and Change, Models* <br>  |
| **Physical Science**  | **UNIT B Exploring With the Senses** <br> Using the senses to observe the physical characteristics of objects; grouping objects by their physical characteristics <br> **Theme:** *Systems* <br><br> **UNIT D Pushes and Pulls** <br> Different ways things move; pushes and pulls; surfaces; directional motion <br> **Themes:** *Systems, Models* | **UNIT C Magnets** <br> The properties of magnets; magnetic force; magnetic fields; temporary magnets; magnets and compasses <br> **Themes:** *Systems, Scale* <br>  | **UNIT B Light and Color** <br> Characteristics of light, such as light sources, how light affects vision, and the way light travels; how shadows are formed and changed; the spectrum and color mixing <br> **Theme:** *Systems* <br><br> **UNIT D Solids, Liquids, and Gases** <br> Properties of solids, liquids, and gases; the changing of materials from one state to another <br> **Theme:** *Constancy and Change* |
| **Earth Science**  | **UNIT C Looking at the Sky** <br> Daytime sky and the Sun; differences between the daytime and nighttime sky; the Moon and the stars <br> **Themes:** *Constancy and Change, Scale* | **UNIT B Weather and Seasons** <br> Factors that affect the weather; seasonal weather changes; how people, plants, and animals respond to weather conditions <br> **Theme:** *Constancy and Change* <br><br> **UNIT D Earth's Land and Water** <br> Properties of soil and rocks; how water and soil mix; how water flows; recycling through composting <br> **Themes:** *Systems, Models* | **UNIT C Earth Through Time** <br> Characteristics of different dinosaurs; how fossil imprints and fossil remains provide clues about Earth's history <br> **Themes:** *Models, Scale, Constancy and Change* <br> 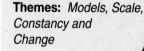 |
| **The Human Body**  | **UNIT E Body Parts** <br> Identification of internal and external body parts; the functions and importance of individual body parts, including the hands, bones, muscles, heart, stomach, and brain <br> **Themes:** *Systems, Models* | **UNIT E Keeping Fit and Healthy** <br> The importance of good nutrition, exercise, sleep, and proper hygiene; the food pyramid and a healthful diet <br> **Themes:** *Systems, Constancy and Change* | **UNIT E What Makes Me Sick** <br> How germs cause illness; how illnesses spread; prevention of illnesses and injuries; how to stay healthy <br> **Themes:** *Systems, Scale* |

> *The science that all students are expected to learn is defined so that students have sufficient time to develop a deep understanding of essential scientific ideas rather than superficial acquaintance with many isolated facts.*
>
> National Science Education Standards

## GRADE 3

**UNIT A  Life Cycles**
Stages in the life cycles of animals and plants; changes in animals and plants as they mature; ways that animals and plants survive
**Theme:** *Models*

**UNIT E  Roles of Living Things**
The needs of living things in relation to their environments; how living things adapt to their environments, change them, and respond to them
**Theme:** *Constancy and Change*

**UNIT C  Forms of Energy**
The forms of energy and their effect on matter; how heat energy moves, changes matter, and is measured; the benefits and drawbacks of different energy sources
**Theme:** *Systems*

**UNIT B  Sun, Moon, and Earth**
The physical features of the Sun and Moon; the rotation and revolution of Earth and the Moon; Earth's seasonal changes; eclipses
**Theme:** *Scale*

**UNIT D  Earth's Water**
Characteristics of Earth's water, including sources of fresh water and the water cycle; water distribution, pollution, and conservation
**Theme:** *Systems*

**UNIT F  What's for Lunch?**
Nutrients and the types and amounts of food in a healthful diet; sanitary food storage and preparation; care of teeth and gums; digestion
**Theme:** *Systems*

## GRADE 4

**UNIT C  Animals**
Basic needs of animals; adaptations that help animals meet their needs; classification of living things; characteristics of different animal groups
**Theme:** *Systems*

**UNIT B  Properties of Matter**
Physical properties; states; effects of heat loss or gain and of physical and chemical changes
**Theme:** *Scale*

**UNIT D  Magnetism and Electricity**
Properties of magnets; forms of electrical energy; electric circuits; sources of electric current; how electric current is changed into useful energy
**Theme:** *Models*

**UNIT A  Earth's Land Resources**
How moving water, wind, and ice shape the land; natural resources and conservation efforts; consequences of producing and disposing of trash
**Theme:** *Constancy and Change*

**UNIT E  Weather and Climate**
Earth's atmosphere; effects of changes in the air on weather; weather patterns and predictions; seasonal weather changes and climate
**Theme:** *Constancy and Change*

**UNIT F  The Body's Delivery Systems**
Organs and functions of the respiratory, circulatory, and excretory systems; health measures that prevent or fight disease; harmful effects of nicotine, alcohol, and other drugs
**Theme:** *Systems*

## GRADE 5

**UNIT A  Plants**
Parts of flowering plants; plant cells; plant processes; classifying plants; structural adaptations
**Theme:** *Systems*

**UNIT D  Populations and Ecosystems**
Dynamic interactions of living and nonliving things in an ecosystem; how energy and matter flow through an ecosystem; biomes; biodiversity
**Theme:** *Systems*

**UNIT C  Energy, Work, and Machines**
Properties of energy, including its forms, ability to change form, and effects; friction; simple machines
**Theme:** *Systems*

**UNIT F  Light and Sound**
Properties of light; lenses and their uses; color; properties of sound; the sense of hearing; controlling, recording, and transmitting sound
**Theme:** *Models*

**UNIT B  The Solar System and Beyond**
The night sky; how astronomers learn about space; the solar system; stars and galaxies; survival in space
**Theme:** *Scale*

**UNIT E  The Solid Earth**
Properties and uses of minerals and rocks; the rock cycle; Earth's structure; fossils as clues to the age of rocks; the formation of mountains; faults
**Theme:** *Constancy and Change*

**UNIT G  Movement and Control**
Organs and functions of the skeletal and muscular systems; avoiding bone and muscle injuries; organs and functions of the nervous system; harmful effects of tobacco, alcohol, and other drugs
**Theme:** *Systems*

## GRADE 6

**UNIT A  Cells and Microbes**
Structure and life processes of cells, including mitosis; protists and fungi; of bacteria and viruses
**Theme:** *Models*

**UNIT D  Continuity of Life**
Asexual reproduction; sexual reproduction, including meiosis; inherited and acquired traits; evolution, including evidence for evolution and evolutionary processes
**Theme:** *Constancy and Change*

**UNIT C  The Nature of Matter**
Physical/chemical properties; elements, compounds, mixtures; physical and chemical changes; acids and bases; atomic structure
**Theme:** *Scale*

**UNIT F  Forces and Motion**
Characteristics of motion; gravity; measuring changes in motion; friction; action/reaction forces; how forces affect the motion of objects
**Theme:** *Scale*

**UNIT B  The Changing Earth**
Theory of plate tectonics; the movement of continents; the formation of mountains; earthquakes and volcanoes
**Theme:** *Models*

**UNIT E  Oceanography**
Contents and properties of ocean water; features and exploration of the ocean floor; currents, waves, and tides; resources from the ocean; ocean pollution
**Theme:** *Systems*

**UNIT G  Growing Up Healthy**
Human reproduction; the endocrine system and the human life cycle; defenses of the immune system; illness and immune system disorders; reducing health risk factors
**Theme:** *Systems*

**The major concepts for a unit are listed on the first page of that unit in this Teaching Guide.**

# How DiscoveryWorks
## Silver Burdett Ginn Science
### in Grades 3-6

The Teaching Guide and Activities and Resources in the Student Edition, together with the supporting Equipment Kits, present strong science content in an exciting and innovative format. Additional materials, including CD-ROM technology, support and expand the concepts in each investigation.

## Trade Book Library

Trade Books in each grade-level library provide in-depth science content, biographies of famous scientists, and science-related fiction. Trade Books can be used to introduce each unit and reinforce investigation concepts.

## Teaching Guide

The *Teaching Guide* is a road-map for moving through the activities and resources.

## Science Notebook

The *Science Notebook* includes space for students to record their observations and conclusions as they work through Activities, Investigate Further Extensions, and Unit Project Links. Used as the basis for a Portfolio, students can use the notebook to generate ideas about concepts and reassess their learning.

## Educational Technology

*SCIENCE PROCESSOR: An Interactive CD-ROM* contains investigations that can be used in place of or as extensions of print materials. Tools such as Grapher and Spreadsheet allow for easy data interpretation. VIDEOTAPES and VIDEODISCS complement specific units.

## Assessment

Portfolio and performance based assessment opportunities are embedded throughout the investigations.

# SAFETY
## An Essential Element

In order for students to develop respect for safety, they need to understand exactly what is meant by safe and unsafe behavior and what the rationale is behind safety rules. Through your teaching as well as your example, students can develop the "safe science" attitudes and skills that are essential both in school and at home.

## General Safety Guidelines

- Post an easy-to-read list of safety rules in a prominent place in the classroom. Review it with students on a regular basis.

- Become familiar with the safety procedures that are necessary for each activity before introducing it to your students.

- Discuss specific safety precautions with students before beginning every hands-on science activity.

- Always act as an exemplary model of safe behavior.

- Have students wear protective aprons, goggles, and gloves whenever these items will prevent injury.

- Keep safety equipment, such as fire blankets and fire extinguishers, readily accessible and know how to use it.

- Prepare students for emergencies by having them practice leaving the classroom quickly and safely.

- Show students how to obtain help in an emergency by using the telephone, an intercom, or other available means of communication.

- Never leave students unattended while they are involved in science activities.

- Provide ample space for science activities that require students to move about and handle materials.

- Keep your classroom and all science materials in proper condition. Check their condition regularly.

- Tell students to report all injuries to you immediately.

For more detailed information on safety, you may wish to order the NSTA publication *Safety in the Elementary Science Classroom* (1993). Write or call the National Science Teachers Association, NSTA Publication Sales, 1840 Wilson Boulevard, Arlington, VA 22201-3000; telephone: (703) 243-7100 or (800) 722-6782.

# MATERIALS LIST

*Below is a complete list of materials needed for all activities included in the Grade 3 student book. Quantities are indicated for a class of 30 students working in groups of 5. Materials included in the Grade Level Equipment Kit are indicated with a (\*).*

## Consumable Materials

| Materials | Quantity | Activity Page Numbers |
|---|---|---|
| aluminum foil* | 1 roll | C6, D13 |
| antacid tablets, calcium-enriched* | 6 tablets | D42 |
| apples | 20 | A20, A22, F6, F42 |
| bag, brown paper* | 6 large squares | F8 |
| bag, plastic* | 1 | C32, C33, C34, |
| bags, self-sealing plastic* | 36 | A38, E15, F32 |
| bologna or other luncheon meat | 6 pieces | F8 |
| bread | 12 slices | E15, F6 |
| bread, nonfat* | 6 slices | F8 |
| carrot slices | 6 slices | D8, F8 |
| celery | 30 stalks | F48 |
| cereal boxes, empty | 36 | F24 |
| cereal, dry (not sugar coated) | 1 box | A20 |
| cheese | 18 slices | E15, F6, F8 |
| cheesecloth* | 12 squares | D22, D46 |
| clay, modeling* | 8 boxes | B34, B62, C6, C24 |
| cones, conifer* | assortment | A50 |
| cookies | 6 | F8 |
| cotton swabs* | 1 box | A44 |
| crackers, small pieces | 1 box | A22 |
| craft sticks, wooden* | 6 | C30 |
| crickets | 36–48 | A22 |
| cups, paper* | 70 | A58, C57, D56, D73, E6 |
| cups, paper (small)* | 90 cups | D40 |
| cups, small plastic | 6 | D20 |
| dental floss* | 6 rolls | F49 |
| dishwashing liquid* | 1 bottle | D42 |
| eggs, uncooked | 6 | A12 |
| feathers, down* | 4 oz. | E70 |
| fertilizer, liquid* | 12 oz | D48 |
| flowers | 6 | A44 |
| food coloring* | 6 bottles | C24, D66 |
| food packages, empty | 36 | F26 |
| foods: bitter, salty, sour, sweet (each in separate closed containers) | 6 sets | F42 |
| gloves, plastic* | 120 pairs | A12, A20, A22, F32 |
| glucose test strips* | 30 | F54 |
| gravel* | 8 bags | D22, D46, D64 |
| holly cuttings | 6 | E46 |
| index cards* | 2 packages | A28, E24 |
| insulating materials (yarn, cloth, boxes, foil, etc.) | variety | C57 |
| iodine solution | 1 dropper bottle | F6 |
| iron filings* | 6 small jars | B26 |
| juices: apple, cranberry, orange | 1 container of each type of juice | F54 |
| lactase drops* | 6 drops | F54 |
| lettuce | 3 heads | A22 |
| magazines, discarded | several | A28, E22 |
| markers, black* | 6 | B34, D40, E6 |
| matches, safety | 6 | C6 |
| mealworms* | 36 | A20 |
| milk | 1 quart | F54 |
| milk cartons, 1 pt (empty) | 6 | D32 |
| milk cartons, 1/2-pint (empty) | 15 | D73 |
| nail or pencil | 1 | D32 |
| newspaper | as needed | B8, D22, E8, F49 |
| noodles, cooked | 6 | F6 |

paper circles, large . . . . . . . . . . . . . . . . . . . . . . . . . . . . . . . . . 6 . . . . . . . . . . . . . . . . . . . . . . . . . . . . . . . . . . . . . . . . B24
paper, colored . . . . . . . . . . . . . . . . . . . . . . . . . . . . . . . . . variety . . . . . . . . . . . . . . . . . . . . . . . . . . . . . . . . C7, E48
paper, construction . . . . . . . . . . . . . . . . . . . . . . . . . . . . 70 sheets . . . . . . . . . . . . . . . . . . . . . . . . . . . A28, B60
paper, drawing. . . . . . . . . . . . . . . . . . . . . . . . . . . . . . . . 30 sheets . . . . . . . . . . . . . . . . . . . . . . . . . . . . . . . . . B24
paper, large sheets . . . . . . . . . . . . . . . . . . . . . . . . . . . . 12 sheets . . . . . . . . . . . . . . . . . . . . . . . . . . . B24, B34
paper, plain white . . . . . . . . . . . . . . . . . . . . . . . . . . . . . 12 sheets . . . . . . . . . . . . . . . . . . . . . . . . . . . . A6, A44
paper, red* . . . . . . . . . . . . . . . . . . . . . . . . . . . . . . . . . . 30 sheets . . . . . . . . . . . . . . . . . . . . . . . C32, C33, C34
paper towels . . . . . . . . . . . . . . . . . . . . . . . . . . . . . . . . . 1 roll . . . . . . . . . . . . . . . . . . . . . . . . . . . E8, E47, F49
paper, tracing* . . . . . . . . . . . . . . . . . . . . . . . . . . . . . . . 30 sheets . . . . . . . . . . . . . . . . . . . . . . . . . . . . . . . . . . D6
peanut butter . . . . . . . . . . . . . . . . . . . . . . . . . . . . . . . . 1 jar . . . . . . . . . . . . . . . . . . . . . . . . . . . . . . . . . . . . . F49
pear, grated . . . . . . . . . . . . . . . . . . . . . . . . . . . . . . . . 15 samples . . . . . . . . . . . . . . . . . . . . . . . . . . . . . . . . . F42
pencils (with erasers). . . . . . . . . . . . . . . . . . . . . . . . . . 18 . . . . . . . . . . . . . . . . . . . . . . . . . . . . C26, D56, E47
pencils, colored (or markers) . . . . . . . . . . . . . . . . . . . 6 sets . . . . . . . . . . . . . . . A28, D6, E22, E24, E48
pencils, grease* . . . . . . . . . . . . . . . . . . . . . . . . . . . . . . 6 . . . . . . . . . . . . . . . . . . . . . C24, D48, D56, F32
pill bugs* . . . . . . . . . . . . . . . . . . . . . . . . . . . . . . . . . . 36 . . . . . . . . . . . . . . . . . . . . . . . . . . . . . . . . . E8, E47
plastic wrap* . . . . . . . . . . . . . . . . . . . . . . . . . . . . . . . 1 roll . . . . . . . . . . . . . . . . . . . . . . . . . . . . . . A58, D48
plates, paper* . . . . . . . . . . . . . . . . . . . . . . . . . . . . . . . 54 . . . . . . . . . . . . . . . . . . . . . . . . . . . . B26, D6, F42
potato chips . . . . . . . . . . . . . . . . . . . . . . . . . . . . . . . . 6 . . . . . . . . . . . . . . . . . . . . . . . . . . . . . . . . . . . . . . . F8
potatos, raw . . . . . . . . . . . . . . . . . . . . . . . . . . . . . . . . 10 . . . . . . . . . . . . . . . . . . . . . A20, F6, F8, F32, F42
raisins . . . . . . . . . . . . . . . . . . . . . . . . . . . . . . . . . . . . 60 . . . . . . . . . . . . . . . . . . . . . . . . . . . . . . . . . . . . . . E38
rice . . . . . . . . . . . . . . . . . . . . . . . . . . . . . . . . . . . . . . 1 box . . . . . . . . . . . . . . . . . . . . . . . . . . . . . . . . . . . . E38
rose cuttings . . . . . . . . . . . . . . . . . . . . . . . . . . . . . . . 15 . . . . . . . . . . . . . . . . . . . . . . . . . . . . . . . . . . . . . . E46
rubber bands* . . . . . . . . . . . . . . . . . . . . . . . . . . . . . . 1 box . . . . . . . . . . . . . . . . . . . . . D13, D22, D46, D48
rubber bands (strong)* . . . . . . . . . . . . . . . . . . . . . . . 5. . . . . . . . . . . . . . . . . . . . . . . . . . . . . . . . . . . . . . . . C8
sand* . . . . . . . . . . . . . . . . . . . . . . . . . . . . . . . . . . . . 5 bags . . . . . . . . . A22, B8, C14, C16, D20, D22, D46, E38
seedlings, radish or bean . . . . . . . . . . . . . . . . . . . . . . 36 . . . . . . . . . . . . . . . . . . . . . . . . . . . . . . . . . A58, E6
seeds, lima bean* . . . . . . . . . . . . . . . . . . . . . . . . . . . 1 bag . . . . . . . . . . . . . . . . . . . . . . . . . . . . . . . . . . . . A38
seeds, radish* . . . . . . . . . . . . . . . . . . . . . . . . . . . . . . 6 packages. . . . . . . . . . . . . . . . . . . . . . . . . . . . . . . D56
shoeboxes with lids* . . . . . . . . . . . . . . . . . . . . . . . . . 15 or 6. . . . . . . . . . . . . . . . . . . . . . . . . . . . . . . . . . . A58
soil, potting*. . . . . . . . . . . . . . . . . . . . . . . . . . . . . . . 4 lbs . . . . . . . . . . . . . A58, D56, D22, D46, D64, E6
straws, clear plastic* . . . . . . . . . . . . . . . . . . . . . . . . . 12 . . . . . . . . . . . . . . . . . . . . . . . . . . . . . . . . C24, E38
string* . . . . . . . . . . . . . . . . . . . . . . . . . . . . . . . . . . . 1 ball . . . . . . . . . . . . . . . . B6, B18, B24, B60, E22
sugar. . . . . . . . . . . . . . . . . . . . . . . . . . . . . . . . . . . . . 1 box . . . . . . . . . . . . . . . . . . . . . . . . . . . . . . . . . . . . C41
tape, masking* . . . . . . . . . . . . . . . . . . . . . . . . . . . . . 1 roll. . . . . . . . . . . . . . . . . . . . . B18, D32, D34, E47
tape, transparent* . . . . . . . . . . . . . . . . . . . . . . . . . . 1 roll . . . . . A38, A58, B24, B60, E8, E15, E22, E38, E48
toothpicks* . . . . . . . . . . . . . . . . . . . . . . . . . . . . . . . . 1 box . . . . . . . . . . . . . . . . . . . . . . . . . . . . A38, B62, E38
twigs and leaves. . . . . . . . . . . . . . . . . . . . . . . . . . . . . N/A. . . . . . . . . . . . . . . . . . . . . . . . . . . . . . . . . . . . . . D46
vegetable oil* . . . . . . . . . . . . . . . . . . . . . . . . . . . . . . 24 oz . . . . . . . . . . . . . . . . . . . . . . . . . . . . . . . . D64, F8
vinegar, white* . . . . . . . . . . . . . . . . . . . . . . . . . . . . . 24 oz . . . . . . . . . . . . . . . . . . . . . . . . . . . . . . D56, E47
water, aquarium. . . . . . . . . . . . . . . . . . . . . . . . . . . . 300 mL . . . . . . . . . . . . . . . . . . . . . . . . . . . . . . . . . . . D48
water, distilled (teacher only). . . . . . . . . . . . . . . . . . . 1 bottle . . . . . . . . . . . . . . . . . . . . . . . . . . . . . . . . . . D40
water, spring (teacher only) . . . . . . . . . . . . . . . . . . . . 1 bottle . . . . . . . . . . . . . . . . . . . . . . . . . . . . . . . . . . D40
yarn, blue and red* . . . . . . . . . . . . . . . . . . . . . . . . . . 1 skein each . . . . . . . . . . . . . . . . . . . . . . . . . . . . . . . E24

## Nonconsumable Materials

| Materials | Quantity | Activity Page Numbers |
|---|---|---|
| balances and masses* . . . . . . . . . . . . . . . . . . . . . . . . . . | 6 . . . . . . . . . . . . . . . . . . . . . . . . . . . . . . . . | D8 |
| balls, plastic foam (3 in.)* . . . . . . . . . . . . . . . . . . . . . . | 10 . . . . . . . . . . . . . . . . . . . . . . . . . . . . . | B74 |
| balls, white plastic foam (5- or 6-in. size) * . . . . . . . . . . | 10 . . . . . . . . . . . . . . . . . . . . . . . . . . . . . | B50 |
| books, about animals. . . . . . . . . . . . . . . . . . . . . . . . . . | N/A. . . . . . . . . . . . . . . . . . . . . . . . . . . . | A6, E22 |
| book, heavy . . . . . . . . . . . . . . . . . . . . . . . . . . . . . . . . | 6 . . . . . . . . . . . . . . . . . . . . . . . . . . . . . . . . | B18 |
| books, reference . . . . . . . . . . . . . . . . . . . . . . . . . . . . | N/A. . . . . . . . . . . . . . . . . . . . . . . . . . . . | A28 |
| bottles, soda (plastic) . . . . . . . . . . . . . . . . . . . . . . . . . | 6 . . . . . . . . . . . . . . . . . . . . . . . C24, D22, D46 |
| bowls, plastic* . . . . . . . . . . . . . . . . . . . . . . . . . . . . . . | 12 . . . . . . . . . . . . . . . . . . . . . . . . . . . . . . . . | C24 |
| box from which to draw cards . . . . . . . . . . . . . . . . . . . | 6 . . . . . . . . . . . . . . . . . . . . . . . . . . . . . . . . | A28 |
| calculators . . . . . . . . . . . . . . . . . . . . . . . . . . . . . . . . | 6 . . . . . . . . . . . . . . . . . . . . . . . . . . . . . . . . | C56 |
| coat hangers, wire. . . . . . . . . . . . . . . . . . . . . . . . . . . | 30 . . . . . . . . . . . . . . . . . . . . . . . . . . . . . . . . | E22 |
| coffee can lids, plastic. . . . . . . . . . . . . . . . . . . . . . . . . | 10 . . . . . . . . . . . . . . . . . . . . . . . . . . . . . . . . | C8 |
| coffee cans. . . . . . . . . . . . . . . . . . . . . . . . . . . . . . . . | 5. . . . . . . . . . . . . . . . . . . . . . . . . . . . . . . . . | C8 |
| combs, strong and fine-toothed* . . . . . . . . . . . . . . . . . | 6 . . . . . . . . . . . . . . . . . . . . . . . . . . . . . . . . | F49 |
| containers with lids* . . . . . . . . . . . . . . . . . . . . . . . . . | 6 . . . . . . . . . . . . . . . . . . . . . . . . . . . . . E8, E47 |
| cotton cloth* . . . . . . . . . . . . . . . . . . . . . . . . . . . . . . | 12 squares . . . . . . . . . . . . . . . . . . . . . . . . . . . C40 |
| cups, clear plastic* . . . . . . . . . . . . . . . . . . . . . . . . . . | 12. . . . . . . . . . . . . . . . . . C41, D12, D48, F54 |

# UNIT D

# Earth's Water

**Overview** Earth's Water focuses on the importance of water for living things on Earth. Through activities and resources, students learn about the properties of water and how water cycles through Earth's ecosystems. Students will discover properties of water that affect our water supply and learn how we can best care for this crucial resource.

**Theme** Water is essential in systems at every level of biology. On the level of the ecosystem, water is a key habitat for many organisms. Water evaporates from lakes, rivers, and the ocean, forms clouds, and falls as rain or snow, cycling through the world's ecosystems. Water is a crucial nutrient for all body systems. Earth's Water describes a typical water supply system, which helps ensure people have an adequate supply of clean water. Protecting Earth's water supply is important to help safeguard our health and the health of people and organisms in all regions of the world.

## THE BIG IDEA

*Water, an essential natural resource, can be depleted or polluted in places on Earth; it must be conserved and protected for future use.*

## Tracing Major Concepts

**Water, an essential natural resource, is found on Earth's surface, in the atmosphere, and underground.**

### Subconcepts

- Water, which covers almost three-fourths of Earth's surface and is essential for sustaining life, is used by people in many ways.
- As water moves through the water cycle, it changes state as heat energy is added or taken away.
- Our freshwater supplies come from surface water and ground water.

**Water's physical properties affect Earth's water supply.**

### Subconcepts

- Water pressure allows water to flow through pipes; because water expands as it freezes, pipes can break.

- The flavor and other properties of drinking water can vary due to dissolved mineral and chemical content.
- Materials dissolved or suspended in water may make it unfit to drink.

**The availability of Earth's water supplies may not keep up with demands; water can be polluted, yet it also can be conserved and pollution can be reduced.**

### Subconcepts

- Water pollution—caused by agricultural runoff, industries, and home septic systems—can be reduced.
- Water pollution that reaches, or is released into, the ocean is dispersed by tides and currents.
- Water must be conserved—and pollution cleaned up and prevented—in order to insure that there is enough safe fresh water for everyone's basic needs.

# CONTENTS

## Chapter 13   Caring for Our Water . . . . . . . . . . . . . . . . . . . . . . . . . . . . .D54

# Standards & Benchmarks CORRELATIONS

**The National Science Education Standards and Project 2061 Benchmarks\* are the framework around which _Silver Burdett Ginn Science DiscoveryWorks_ is built.**

- Materials can exist in different states—solid, liquid, and gas. Some common materials, such as water, can be changed form one state to another by heating or cooling. (p. 127) *Ch. 1, Inv. 1*

- All organisms cause changes in the environment where they live. Some of these changes are detrimental to the organism or other organisms, whereas others are beneficial. (p. 129) *Ch. 2 and 3*

- Humans depend on their natural and constructed environments. Humans change environments in ways that can be either beneficial or detrimental for themselves and other organisms. (p. 129) *Ch. 1, Inv. 1 and 2; Ch. 2 and 3*

- Scientists and engineers often work in teams with different individuals doing different things that contribute to the results. This understanding focuses primarily on teams working together and secondarily, on the combination of scientist and engineer teams. (p. 138) *Ch. 2, Inv. 3*

- The supply of many resources is limited. If used, resouces can be extended through recycling and decreased use. (p. 140) *Ch. 3, Inv. 1 and 3*

- Science and technology have been practiced by people for a long time. (p. 141) *Entire Unit*

---

- When liquid water disappears, it turns into a gas (vapor) in the air and can reappear as a liquid when cooled, or as a solid if cooled below the freezing point of water. Clouds and fog are made of tiny droplets of water. (p. 68) *Ch. 1, Inv. 2*

- Things on or near the earth are pulled toward it by the earth's gravity. (p. 68) *Ch. 2, Inv. 1*

\*Standards are based on _National Science Education Standards_ (© 1996) published by The National Research Council. Benchmarks are based on _Benchmarks for Science Literacy_ (© 1993) published by The American Association for the Advancement of Science.

# Curriculum
# INTEGRATION

S cience as a discipline does not exist in isolation. An integrated approach to the teaching of science will help students understand how science connects to other school subjects as well as to technology, to diverse cultures, and to literature. The location in the unit of activities that connect to other disciplines is indicated in the chart.

## THE SCIENCES

- Life Science, page D10
- Life Science, page D16
- Life Science, page D49
- Life Science, page D50
- Life Science, page D58
- Physical Science, page D59
- Earth Science, page D76

## LITERATURE

- Water Paths, page D41
- Science in Literature features, pages D17, D37, D60

## MATH

- Fractions, page D9
- Totaling, page D24
- Burst Pipe, page D37
- Graphing, page D44

## LANGUAGE ARTS

- Writing Poems, page D36
- Writing Laws, page D60

## CONNECTING SCIENCE TO

## CULTURAL CONNECTIONS

- Experimenting, page D14
- Using Maps, page D25
- Picture Story, page D38
- Carrying Water, page D51
- Ocean Currents, page D68
- Aqueducts, page D75

## SOCIAL STUDIES

- Analyzing, page D26
- Make a Map, page D70

## TECHNOLOGY & SOCIETY

- Dry Ice, page D15
- Making Models, page D18
- Water Supply, page D43
- Experiment, page D61
- Writing Guides, page D74
- Solutions, page D77

## THE ARTS

- Cartooning, page D17
- Drawing, page D62
- Composing, page D67

# Water: The Stuff of Life

## Dr. Lowell J. Bethel

*Dr. Lowell J. Bethel received his bachelor's and his master's degrees from Temple University, and he received his doctoral degree from the University of Pennsylvania. Dr Bethel is now teaching at the University of Texas at Austin.*

### LIVING THINGS NEED WATER

By weight, the human body is about 67 percent water. To stay healthy, people need to drink about two to three quarts of water, or beverages made mainly of water, every day. Most people would die of complications due to dehydration after few days without water. Likewise, most animals and plants cannot survive long without taking in water.

### IMPORTANT PROPERTIES OF WATER

Water's chemical formula is $H_2O$. This formula indicates that water is composed of two elements: each water molecule contains two atoms of hydrogen ($H_2$) for every atom of oxygen (O).

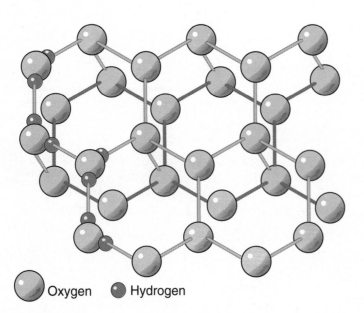

○ Oxygen   ● Hydrogen

The shape of a water molecule and the nature of the bonds between its atoms help determine some of water's most important properties. For instance, ice (frozen water) is an unusual solid in that it is less dense than water in its liquid form. (Most solids are more dense than the same material in a liquid state.) Water molecules arrange themselves in a crystalline lattice when the temperature drops below 0°C (32°F). In the lattice, the molecules have much empty space between them as shown in the drawing. When the ice melts, the lattice structure begins to break down, and the water molecules crowd together.

These contrasting properties of ice and liquid water have important consequences for life on Earth. For instance, ice that forms on bodies of water during the winter helps keep water-dwellers alive. The ice, floating on the surface, insulates the water from the cold air above it. This helps hold the water temperature steady just above freezing, a temperature at which most living things can survive. If ice were denser than water, it would sink to the bottom. Without the insulating ice cap, the water would probably freeze solid killing the water-dwelling animals and plants.

Freezing temperatures are damaging to living things because the water inside the cells can freeze. As it freezes, the crystalline structure causes the water to expand. Many cells rupture, just as water-filled pipes burst when the water inside them freezes.

◀ **The structure of ice. The hydrogen atoms are omitted for all but four water molecules.**

# TIPS FROM Teachers

Have students talk about what it would mean to build a small hydroelectric power plant on a stream. How would it affect the surrounding area? Would it help people? Could it cause problems? Have students debate the question of whether more energy is always desirable.

*Rodney Petersheim
Enola,
Pennsylvania*

I use the overhead projector to help students observe properties of water. On a clear plastic sheet on the projector stage, I place a teaspoonful of water. Students can see the water spread and seek a low spot. The light projected through the water shows shadows, which indicate the water's surface is not flat. I invite students to experiment with the water. One idea is to sprinkle pepper over the surface and use a utensil to try to collect the grains!

*Judy Kay Henry
Billings, Montana*

To extend our unit on water, I discuss water's surface tension. To demonstrate the property of surface tension, have students use eyedroppers to drip water onto a piece of waxed paper then observe the drops from eye level. Discuss why the drops appear as small hills, with a rounded shape, rather than as flat disks. Then have students dip a toothpick in liquid soap and stick it into the water drops to break them up.

*Kathleen M.
Groeschen
Des Plaines, Illinois*

# Skills for LIFELONG LEARNING

Experiences provided by *Silver Burdett Ginn Science DiscoveryWorks* are aimed at developing a wide range of science processes and skills. These tools provide a basis for a lifetime of participation in society as a whole. As described in *Science for All Americans* by F. James Rutherford and Andrew Ahlgren (Oxford University Press, 1990), the skills developed through scientific inquiry foster reasoning abilities that relate directly to a person's outlook on knowledge and learning and ways of thinking and acting.

**Process Skills** provide a framework in which ideas can be conceptualized, tested, and evaluated. The processes listed here are developed through a wide range of hands-on experiences.

## Process Skills

| Activities | Page | Observing | Classifying | Measuring/Using Numbers | Communicating | Inferring | Predicting | Collecting, Recording, and Interpreting Data | Identifying and Controlling Variables | Defining Operationally | Making Hypotheses | Experimenting | Making and Using Models |
|---|---|---|---|---|---|---|---|---|---|---|---|---|---|
| The Water Planet | D6 | | • | • | • | • | • | | | | | | |
| Dry Up! | D8 | | | • | | • | | • | | | | • | |
| Disappearing Act | D12 | • | | • | | | | | • | • | • | | |
| Water Ups and Downs | D13 | • | | | | | • | | • | • | | | |
| Well, Well | D20 | • | | | | • | • | | | | | | |
| Soak It Up! | D22 | | • | | | • | • | • | | | | | |
| The Pressure's On | D32 | • | | | | • | • | | | • | • | • | |
| Tower Power | D34 | • | | | | • | | • | | | | | |
| Water Taste-Test | D40 | • | • | | • | • | | | | | | | |
| Hard and Soft Water | D42 | • | • | | | • | | • | • | | | • | |
| Let's Clear This Up | D46 | | • | | | | • | | | • | • | • | |
| Not As Clear As It Looks | D48 | • | | • | | • | | • | • | | | | |
| Not-So-Gentle Rain | D56 | • | | | | | • | | • | | | | |
| All Washed Up | D64 | | | | • | | | | | | | | • |
| Going My Way? | D66 | • | | | • | • | | | | | • | | |
| Down the Drain | D72 | | | • | • | • | | • | | | | | |
| Drops Count | D73 | | | • | | • | | • | | | | | |

**Critical Thinking Skills** are embedded in the questioning strategies throughout the program. The chart below summarizes the processes assessed in the Think It/Write It sections that end each investigation.

# Critical Thinking Skills

| Process | Description | D11 | D19 | D28 | D39 | D45 | D52 | D63 | D71 | D78 |
|---------|-------------|-----|-----|-----|-----|-----|-----|-----|-----|-----|
| **Analyzing** | Studying something to identify constituent elements or relationships among elements | • | | • | • | | | | | |
| **Synthesizing** | Using deductive reasoning to pull together key elements | | • | | • | • | • | | • | • |
| **Evaluating** | Reviewing and responding critically to materials, procedures, or ideas and judging them by purposes, standards, or other criteria | | | | • | | | • | | • |
| **Applying** | Using ideas, processes, or skills in new situations | | | | • | | • | • | | |
| **Generating Ideas** | Expressing thoughts that reveal originality, speculation, imagination, a personal perspective, flexibility in thinking, invention, or creativity | | | | | • | • | • | | |
| **Expressing Ideas** | Presenting ideas clearly and in logical order, while using language that is appropriate for the audience and occasion | • | • | • | | • | | • | | • |
| **Solving Problems** | Using critical thinking processes to find solutions to a problem | • | • | • | • | | | • | | • |

Through the development and reinforcement of science process skills and critical thinking skills, the following **Scientific Reasoning Skills** are developed. This symbol identifies questions within the teaching material that highlight Scientific Reasoning Skills.

# Scientific Reasoning Skills

| Reasoning Skill | Description |
|-----------------|-------------|
| **Longing to Know and Understand** | The desire to probe, find information, and seek explanations |
| **Questioning of Scientific Assumptions** | The tendency to hold open for further verification of presented assumptions, encounters, and ideas |
| **Search for Data and Its Meaning** | The propensity to collect information and to analyze it in context |
| **Demand for Verification** | The inclination to repeat and replicate findings and studies |
| **Respect for Logic** | The inclination to move from assumptions to testing and data collection to conclusions |
| **Consideration of Premises** | The tendency to put into context the reason for a particular point of view |
| **Consideration of Consequences** | The tendency to put into perspective the results of a particular point of view |
| **Respect for Historical Contributions** | The inclination to understand and learn from the contributions of earlier ideas, studies, events, and so on |

# Ongoing Assessment

Daily observations and a variety of ongoing assessment activities can provide comprehensive appraisal of student growth. *Silver Burdett Ginn Science DiscoveryWorks* provides several methods to help you monitor student growth.

## Performance Assessment

Observation checklists provide concrete descriptions of student behaviors. Performance assessments allow students to demonstrate their ability to use the tools of science and science processes in hands-on activities, at the end of each investigation and chapter, and in a culminating unit performance task.

## Portfolio Assessment

Portfolios of student work can be used to holistically assess student understanding and progress. The *Assessment Guide* provides support materials for developing portfolios and in using them to evaluate growth in science.

## Written Reviews and Tests

Think It/Write It sections at the end of each investigation foster critical thinking and provide a snapshot of student understanding. Written tests provide additional tools for assessing how well students understand, integrate, and apply key concepts. Opportunities for periodic review are included in Analyze and Conclude at the end of each activity, in Reflect and Evaluate at the end of each chapter, and in Chapter Tests and Unit Tests in the *Assessment Guide*.

## Unit Performance Assessment

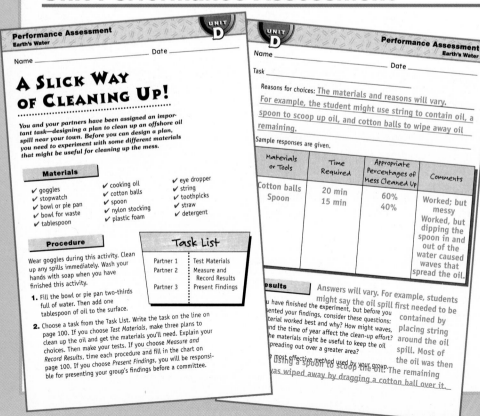

**Performance Assessment**
Earth's Water

UNIT D

Name _____ Date _____

### A SLICK WAY OF CLEANING UP!

*You and your partners have been assigned an important task—designing a plan to clean up an offshore oil spill near your town. Before you can design a plan, you need to experiment with some different materials that might be useful for cleaning up the mess.*

**Materials**

✔ goggles
✔ stopwatch
✔ bowl or pie pan
✔ bowl for waste
✔ tablespoon

✔ cooking oil
✔ cotton balls
✔ spoon
✔ nylon stocking
✔ plastic foam

✔ eye dropper
✔ string
✔ toothpicks
✔ straw
✔ detergent

**Procedure**

Wear goggles during this activity. Clean up any spills immediately. Wash your hands with soap when you have finished this activity.

1. Fill the bowl or pie pan two-thirds full of water. Then add one tablespoon of oil to the surface.

2. Choose a task from the Task List. Write the task on the line on page 100. If you choose *Test Materials*, make three plans to clean up the oil and get the materials you'll need. Explain your choices. Then make your tests. If you choose *Measure and Record Results*, time each procedure and fill in the chart on page 100. If you choose *Present Findings*, you will be responsible for presenting your group's findings before a committee.

**Task List**

| | |
|---|---|
| Partner 1 | Test Materials |
| Partner 2 | Measure and Record Results |
| Partner 3 | Present Findings |

---

UNIT D

**Performance Assessment**
Earth's Water

Name _____ Date _____

Task _____

Reasons for choices: The materials and reasons will vary. For example, the student might use string to contain oil, a spoon to scoop up oil, and cotton balls to wipe away oil remaining.

Sample responses are given.

| Materials or Tools | Time Required | Appropriate Percentages of Mess Cleaned Up | Comments |
|---|---|---|---|
| Cotton balls Spoon | 20 min 15 min | 60% 40% | Worked; but messy Worked, but dipping the spoon in and out of the water caused waves that spread the oil. |

Results — Answers will vary. For example, students might say the oil spill first needed to be contained by placing string around the oil spill. Most of the oil was then ... most effective method used by your group. Using a spoon to scoop the oil. The remaining ...was wiped away by dragging a cotton ball over it.

...u have finished the experiment, but before you ...sented your findings, consider these questions: ...terial worked best and why? How might waves, ...nd the time of year affect the clean-up effort? ...he materials might be useful to keep the oil ...preading out over a greater area?

## PORTFOLIO ASSESSMENT

Choose among the following products students can put in their Portfolios.

- data from activities
- data from Video, Videodisc, or CD-ROM projects
- data from outside research
- integrated curriculum projects
- projects from Investigate Further activities
- results from Think It-Write It activities

# Ongoing Assessment Opportunities

| | Performance | Portfolio | Written Reviews and Tests |
|---|---|---|---|
| **Chapter 1** | | | D29, AG 87–88 |
| *Investigation 1* | | TG D11 | D11, AG 84 |
| *Investigation 2* | TG D19 | | D19, AG 85 |
| *Investigation 3* | TG D28 | | D28, AG 86 |
| **Chapter 2** | | | D53, AG 92–93 |
| *Investigation 1* | TG D39 | | D39, AG 89 |
| *Investigation 2* | | TG D45 | D45, AG 90 |
| *Investigation 3* | TG D52 | | D52, AG 91 |
| **Chapter 3** | | | D79, AG 97–98 |
| *Investigation 1* | | TG D63 | D63, AG 94 |
| *Investigation 2* | | TG D71 | D71, AG 95 |
| *Investigation 3* | TG D78 | | D78, AG 96 |
| **Unit Close** | AG 99–100 | | AG 103–106 |

Key: TG = Teacher Guide    TRB = Teacher Resource Book    All other pages are from the Student Edition.

## Unit Tests

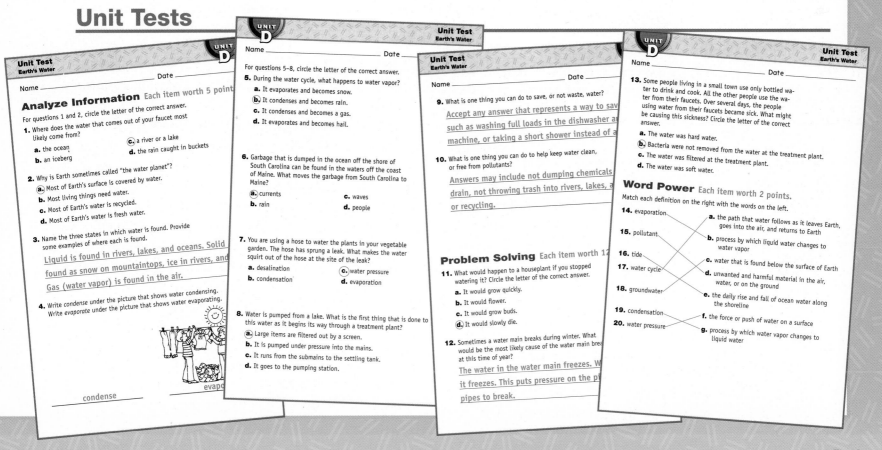

# PROJECT FILE

**UNIT PROJECT**

# Designing a Water Supply System

**Students select a water source for Waterville; they design and construct a model to show how water is cleaned and transported; and they create a "Conserve and Care" calendar.**

## Getting Ready

### Group Size
### *3 to 4 students*

Have each group study the Waterville Brochure and the map of Waterville and recommend a water source for the town. Have different groups design different parts of the system. Then have the class put together the water supply system in a model of the town.

### Materials

#### *For Models and Presentations*

- Assorted material, such as boxes, funnels, rubber tubing, straws, paper clips, modeling clay, scissors, string, tape, and construction paper

### Other Materials

- Unit Project Masters D1–D5, TRB pp. 64–68
- *Science Notebook*, pp. 169, 179, 200

### Plan Ahead

You may wish to invite a representative from the local water utility company to visit the class and answer questions about water systems. Decide where each group can store their part of the project for the duration of the unit.

## Building the Project
### Through Project Links

**Chapter 1, p. D23** Have students cut out Unit Project Masters D2–D5 (TRB pp. 65–68) and tape them together to form one large map of Waterville. Have students work in groups to brainstorm a list of questions about choosing and

designing a water system for Waterville. Combine the questions into one class list. Then have the students work in groups to answer their questions by studying the Waterville Brochure Unit Project Master D1 (TRB p. 64) and looking at the map. Students may use *Science Notebook* p. 169 for their answers. Each group should come up with a decision about the best source of water for the new community along with the reasons for choosing the particular water source. Discuss the choices and come up with a class consensus as to the best source of water for Waterville.

**Assessing Student Progress:** Students should be able to describe some of the water needs of Waterville. Students should be able to give reasons for the choice of a water source for the town.

**Chapter 2, p. D35** Have students work in groups to design the water system for Waterville. Divide the project into several smaller projects such as how to move the water from source to town, how to clean the water, how to store the water, how to move water to buildings, and how to dispose of waste water. Each group could prepare a feasible design for one part of Waterville's water system and report to the class the reasons for their decisions. Students may use *Science Notebook* p. 179 for their plans. The class should approve each part of the design or make changes that will provide a better water system. Each group can build its part of Waterville's system and the parts can be combined to make a whole model of the water system.

**Assessing Student Progress:** Students should be able to track the flow of water from the source to homes and businesses in Waterville. Students should

- **Publish a Guide.** Investigate the trip water takes to get to your home. Draw pictures to show the route the water follows to get to your home. Identify the water's source and describe the water filtering process. Publish your guide to help other people understand how water gets from its source to the home.

- **Write a Report on Sewage Treatment.** Read encyclopedias and other books to learn more about sewage treatment in the United States and why it is so important. Use the information you gain to write a short report. Make a drawing to illustrate your report.

## PEOPLE TO CONTACT

### In Person

- Contact a civil engineer to talk to the class about the design and supervision of the construction of water supply and sewage systems.

### By Mail

- **Water Quality Partnership Adopt-a-School Program, E. I. duPont de Nemours & Company, Inc.,** 400 Woodland Road, Seaford, DE 19973

- **Fresh-Water Foundation,** 725 County Road 6, Wayzata, MN 55391

### By Computer

- Connect to the *SilverShare Bulletin Board* to exchange data and the results of your investigations with other *Silver Burdett Ginn Science DiscoveryWorks* users. Watch for our Internet address, coming soon!

## PLACES TO VISIT

- **Water conservation and treatment Facilities** are a source of information on efforts being made to clear blighted rivers and lakes and make them fit for use again.

- **Primary-sewage-treatment plants** reveal the process of purifying water.

- **Streams in local parks** are a source of information on the quality of local water resources.

be able to describe the reasons for the various parts of the water system that make up the class model.

*Project Link* **Chapter 3, p. D69** Have the class brainstorm a list of messages on conserving water and preventing pollution, twelve of which will be chosen for the "Conserve and Care" calendar. Students may use *Science Notebook* p. 200 for their lists. Each group should produce an artfully decorated paper for each saying assigned to it. Each group can make their own calendar or combine the work of all groups into a master calendar.

**Assessing Student Progress:** Students should be able to name at least twelve ways of conserving or preventing pollution.

## Wrapping Up the Project

## Presenting Waterville

At the completion of the Waterville project hold a Big Event to present the project to other classes and visitors. Tasks students may choose include:

- Describe the town of Waterville.
- Explain the different sources of water considered in designing the water system.
- Explain how water is transported to Waterville.
- Explain how the water is cleaned and stored.
- Explain how water is transported to homes.
- Follow the path of waste water to sewage treatment.
- Describe how the water can be wasted and polluted.
- Describe ways people in Waterville protect and conserve water.

At the end of the event, copies of the "Conserve and Care" calendar may be presented to special visitors.

# Earth's Water

**Overview** CD-ROM activities for this unit enable students to explore how water is used and reused on Earth. They learn about the water cycle and the treatment of water and waste water by creating animated models. They test their water knowledge by determining how water can be conserved in an apartment. This CD-ROM unit consists of five parts: a unit opening and four investigations.

## Using the CD-ROM

### Unit Opening  Water Everywhere (*Beginning the Unit*)

Students begin by listing ways they use water. Then they predict how much of Earth is covered by water, checking their predictions by studying a circle graph. Students use a Water Meter probe to find out how much of Earth's water is liquid or solid and how much is fresh water or salt water. After students record their results on the Spreadsheet, they explore how much fresh water is available for people's use. Students finish by writing about a day without water. This section can also be used with Chapter 1, Inv. 1, 2, and 3.

### Investigation 1 What Goes Around (*Enhances or replaces Chapter 1, Inv. 2*)

**What is the water cycle?**

Through on-screen animation, students observe the water cycle and learn about its stages by clicking on labels and hearing audio clues. Then they drag and drop labels in the appropriate parts of the cycle. When all the parts of the cycle are labeled correctly, the animation begins.

### Investigation 2  Water Works (*Enhances or replaces Chapter 2, Inv. 3*)

**How is water treated and used?**

In this investigation, students explore how a water treatment plant processes water. They begin by watching a video about water treatment. After listening to audio clues, they click on and drag parts of a water treatment system together. Each piece animates when correctly placed. Next, students predict who uses the most water: homes, factories, businesses, or public uses. They click on a graph to check their predictions.

### Investigation 3  Using Water (*Enhances or replaces Chapter 3, Inv. 3*)

**How much water is used each day?**

In this investigation, students explore how much water is used and wasted at home. They use a Water Meter probe to find out how much water is used for each household fixture (kitchen sink, washing machine, shower/tub, bathroom sink, toilet) each day by a family of four. Then they check the data on the Spreadsheet to see the total amount of water an average family of four uses daily.

### Investigation 4  Nice Save (*Enhances or replaces Chapter 3, Inv. 3*)

**How can water be conserved?**

Now that students know that an average family of four uses 400 gallons of water each day, they'll hypothesize how much water can be conserved each day. Students click on each water-using fixture to find out how much water can be saved when using water-saving ideas. Then they predict which daily activity can help conserve the most water, using a Water Meter probe to check their predictions. Students record their results on the Spreadsheet and study the bar graph to compare water use with and without water-saving ideas. Students will then calculate how much water is saved in a week, a month, and a year by using the water-saving ideas. Finally, students watch a video to see what happens to waste water after it enters the drain.

**CD-ROM Interactive**

The CD-ROM includes Data Packs and Tools that can be used to enhance Earth's Water.

## Using the Data Packs

The Data Packs listed below can be accessed for information that relates to this unit.

| | |
|---|---|
| **Clouds** | **Lakes** |
| **Oceans and Seas** | **Rivers** |

## Using the Tools

On-screen tools can help students report results of activities, produce reports, or organize data.

**Spreadsheet**   Students can chart the absorbency of different materials in Soak It Up! in Chapter 1. They can also record their observations of the effects of acid rain on radish plants in Chapter 3.

**Grapher**   Students can use this tool to create a water/land pie graph in Chapter 1.

**Painter**   Students may wish to use this tool to draw a picture of their coastline water model to show in which direction the hot water moved in the Going My Way? activity in Chapter 3.

**Calculator**   Students may want to use this tool to add the number of gallons of water used in the Down the Drain activity in Chapter 3.

**Timer**   Students can use this tool to time the well and the absorbent materials activities in Chapter 1.

## OTHER TECHNOLOGY RESOURCES

**Science DiscoveryWorks**

### Videodisc Problem

*Gone Fishing: Where Have All the Fish Gone?* Students explore air pollution, wind, and rain to find out how a city can destroy fish in a lake that is hundreds of miles away. Use anywhere in this unit.

### Videos

*Journey of the Blob*   Students explore the water cycle and environmental questions concerning water as they follow a boy's journey to dispose of a green blob he has made. Use with Chapter 1 or 3. (Bullfrog Films: 1–800–543–FROG)

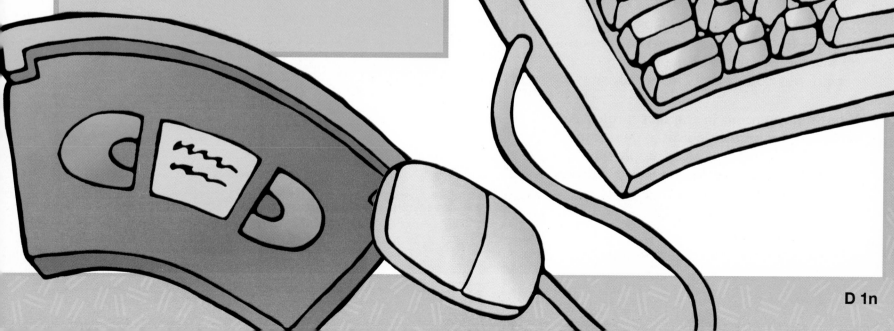

# UNIT D

## Earth's Water

## GET READY TO INVESTIGATE!

### Overview

In this unit, students will be learning about where water sources are found and how nature moves water. They will also learn about what happens to water in pipes, what things in water can be harmful, how water is treated, and how water pollution spreads. The unit will end with how to save and protect water.

### Warming Up

As students look at pages D2–D3, stimulate discussion with these questions:

- **Look at the photograph in the first column. How do you think water gets to your home? From where does this water come?**

- **How do you think the students in the photograph in the second column are cleaning dirty water? How can experimenting and hypothesizing help us make new discoveries about water?**

- Point out the book cover. Invite students to read the summaries. The book pictured is from the Trade Book Library. **What reasons might people have for expressing concern about sources of clean water?**

- **What's happening in the last photo? As we work through this unit, think about some of the ways you can apply what you learn in designing the water supply system for a town.**

 Have students use *Science Notebook* p. 155.

**D 2**

## GET READY TO

### OBSERVE & QUESTION

**Where are sources of fresh water found?**

Think about where the water you use every day comes from. Is it brought by pipes from a far-away reservoir like the one shown? Does it come from a well drilled deep in the ground? Or does it come from some other source?

### EXPERIMENT & HYPOTHESIZE

**What things in water can be harmful?**

Building a model of a water-filtering system will help you investigate how water that is dirty and unsafe is made clean and safe for drinking.

D2

## Home-School Connection

The Opening Letter at the beginning of the unit introduces family members to the topic of how people use Earth's water resources. Distribute the Opening Letter (TRB p.15) at the start of the unit.

**Opening Letter**

### Dear Family,

Even though Earth is a watery planet, the amount of clean, usable, fresh water is limited. In the unit our class is just beginning, we'll discover how people get and use water and how this use affects the quality of Earth's water.

Help your student become aware of the three states of water. Watch the weather for rain, snow, clouds, or fog for examples of water in its liquid and solid states. Water in its gas state is invisible water vapor, but you can feel it when the humidity is high. Find out more about how people affect Earth's water by checking the news for stories on acid rain, oil spills, toxic wastes leaks, and other forms of water pollution.

For this unit, we'll also be using the materials listed below. Can you donate any of these items? If so, we need to receive them by _____.

- aluminum foil
- aluminum pie pans
- cheesecloth
- cooking oil
- empty, paper milk cartons, (1-pt or 1-qt size)
- small jars (with lids)

- liquid dish detergent
- liquid fertilizer (plant food)
- newspaper
- paper cups
- paper plates
- plastic cups, (3-oz, 5-oz)

- plastic soda bottles, (1-L and 2-L)
- potting soil
- radish seeds
- sealable plastic bags
- white vinegar

Do you or other family members have a special interest in or experience with the water cycle, water sources, water treatment, water usage, or water pollution? Could you help with activities? If so, please fill out the form below and have your student return it to class.

Thank you for your help!

- - - - - - - - - - - - - - - - - - - - - - - - - - - - - - - - - ✂

**Opening Letter**
**Earth's Water**

Your name _____ Student's name _____

Home phone _____ Work phone _____

# INVESTIGATE!

## RESEARCH & ANALYZE

**As you investigate, find out more from these books.**

- **DRIP DROP Water's Journey** by Eve and Albert Stwertka (Julian Messner, 1991). Have you ever wondered how water comes out of your faucet, and what happens to water that goes down the drain? This book will tell you.

- **Cloudy With a Chance of Meatballs** by Judi Barrett (Aladdin Books, 1978). Can you imagine what would happen if the water cycle changed into the food cycle? Read this book to find out what happens when food falls from the sky.

## WORK TOGETHER & SHARE IDEAS

**What's your plan for a water supply system for Waterville?**

Working with classmates, you'll have a chance to design and build a model of a town called Waterville. In a group you'll plan

- where the water for your new town will come from.

- how the water will be made safe.

- how the water will be moved to the buildings.

- how to care for and conserve the water.

Then you can display your model town and share your new knowledge with others.

D3

## Additional Student Resources

**Professor Fergus Fahrenheit and his Wonderful Weather Machine** by Candace Groth-Fleming (Simon & Schuster Books for Young Readers, 1994). Based on an incident in which a California town paid a "rainmaker" to end a drought. **(Text Correlation: Chapter 1)**

**The Magic School Bus at the Waterworks** by Joanna Cole (Scholastic, 1986). All children love the humor in this mixture of science fact and fantasy.
**(Text Correlation: Chapter 2)**

**Oceans** by Seymour Simon (Morrow Junior Books, 1990). Photos and text about the ocean floor, currents, tides, tsunamis, waves, storms, coastal erosion, and ocean life.
**(Text Correlation: Chapter 3)**

# BOOKS AND ARTICLES FOR TEACHERS

**Environmental Experiments About Water** by Thomas R. Rybolt (Enslow Publishers, 1993). Presents experiments that focus on the properties of water, its cycle in nature, pollution problems, and methods of purification.

**Healing the Planet: Strategies for Resolving the Environmental Crisis** by Paul R. Ehrlich (Addison-Wesley, 1991). Information on the environment in general, with separate chapters on pollution of water and abuse of water. Information may be used to initiate classsroom discussion.

**How the Earth Works** by John Farndon. (Readers Digest Association, 1992). Guide to Earth science secrets through experiments and hands-on projects. Separate chapters are devoted to rocks and soil and the changing face of the land.

**"Make Your Students Water-Wise: Teaching Water Conservation and Management Through Experiments"** by Lynne Kepler (*Instructor*, Vol. 103, no. 9, May-June 1994, p. 26). Helps students learn about the importance of water conservation and management through experiments.

**Water: Opposing Viewpoints** edited by Carol Wekesser (Greenhaven Press, 1994). Presents opposing viewpoints on issues relating to water, including managing the water supply, acid rain, and government regulations. Good discussion on reducing water pollution. Includes a list of organizations to contact, bibliographies for periodicals, and a separate bibliography.

**Water, Stones, and Fossil Bones** edited by Karen K. Lund (National Science Teachers Association, 1991). Contains a variety of challenging, teacher-tested Earth science activities for elementary and intermediate grades.

# CHAPTER 1

# WATER, WATER EVERYWHERE

| Subconcepts | Activities | Materials |
|---|---|---|
| **Investigation 1  Where Is Water Found on Earth and Why Is Water Important?** | | |
| Water, which covers almost three-fourths of Earth's surface and is essential for sustaining life, is used by people in many ways.<br><br>*Suggested Pacing:  2–3 class periods*<br><br>**Standards**<br>pp. 127, 129, 141<br><br>**Benchmarks**<br>p. 169 | **The Water Planet,** p. D6<br>*Science Processes:*  classify, measure/use numbers, communicate, infer, predict<br><br>**Dry Up!,** p. D8<br>*Science Processes:*  measure/use numbers; infer; collect, record, and interpret data; experiment | metric ruler*, paper plate*, colored markers, tracing paper*, scissors, Activity Support Master D1 (TRB p. 40), *Science Notebook* p. 159<br><br>carrot slice, balance and masses*, pie pan*, *Science Notebook* p. 161 |
| **Investigation 2  How Does Nature Move Water?** | | |
| As water moves through the water cycle, it changes state as heat energy is added or taken away.<br><br>*Suggested Pacing:  2–3 class periods*<br><br>**Standards**<br>pp. 129, 141<br><br>**Benchmarks**<br>pp. 68, 169 | **Disappearing Act,** p. D12<br>*Science Processes:*  observe, measure/use numbers, define operationally, make hypotheses, experiment<br><br>**Water Ups and Downs,** p. D13<br>*Science Processes:*  observe; collect, record, and interpret data; define operationally; make hypotheses | metric measuring cup*, water, 2 plastic cups*, grease pencil*, *Science Notebook* p. 163<br><br>goggles*, plastic jar*, aluminum foil*, hot tap water, rubber band*, ice cubes, *Science Notebook* p. 164 |
| **Investigation 3  Where Are Sources of Fresh Water Found?** | | |
| Our freshwater supplies come from surface water and ground water.<br><br>*Suggested Pacing:  3–4 class periods*<br><br>**Standards**<br>pp. 141, 169 | **Well, Well,** p. D20<br>*Science Processes:*  observe, infer, predict<br><br>**Soak It Up!,** p. D22<br>*Science Processes:*  classify; predict; collect, record, and interpret data; identify and control variables | goggles*, small pie pan*, sand, small soft-plastic cup with the bottom cut off*, plastic spoon*, water, timer*, *Science Notebook* pp. 166–167<br><br>goggles*, newspaper, plastic soda bottle cut in half, cheesecloth*, rubber band*, gravel*, metric measuring cup*, water, timer*, plastic dish, sand*, soil*, *Science Notebook* p. 168 |

# Overview

In this chapter students will investigate water's importance on Earth, discover how heat affects the state of water, and find out where fresh water supplies are found.

## Chapter Concept

Water, an essential natural resource, is found on the Earth's surface, in the atmosphere, and underground.

| Advance Preparation | Curriculum Connection | Assessment |
|---|---|---|
| **The Water Planet**<br>None<br><br>**Dry Up!**<br>If you want to complete the activity in one day, put the pan of carrot slices into a toaster oven at 140°F for a few minutes, turning them over until they feel dry. You also can use potatoes and apples. | Math TG p. D9<br>Integrating the Sciences TG p. D10 | **Chapter 1 Baseline Assessment:**<br>*Science Notebook* pp. 157–158<br><br>**Investigation 1 Baseline Assessment:**<br>TG p. D6<br>**Investigation 1 Review:** AG p. 84<br>**Think It/ Write It,** p. D11; *Science Notebook* p. 162<br>**Following Up on Baseline Assessment:** TG p. D11<br>**Portfolio:** TG p. D11 |
| **Disappearing Act**<br>None<br><br><br><br>**Water Ups and Downs**<br>None | Cultural Connection TG p. D14<br>Science, Technology & Society TG pp. D15, D18<br>Integrating the Sciences TG p. D16<br>The Arts TG p. D17 | **Investigation 2 Baseline Assessment:**<br>TG p. D12<br>**Investigation 2 Review:** AG p. 85<br>**Think it/Write It,** p. D19; *Science Notebook* p. 165<br>**Following Up on Baseline Assessment:** TG p. D19<br>**Performance:** TG p. D19 |
| **Well, Well**<br>None<br><br><br>**Soak It Up!**<br>Cut the soda bottles so that the top half can be used as a funnel. The bottom portion will be used to catch the filtered water. Be sure the funnel is deep enough to accommodate layers of gravel, sand, and soil. Save the cut bottles for future use. | Math TG p. D24<br>Cultural Connection TG p. D25<br>Social Studies TG p. D26 | **Investigation 3 Baseline Assesssment:**<br>TG p. D20<br>**Investigation 3 Review:** AG p. 86<br>**Think It/Write It,** p. D28; *Science Notebook* p. 170<br>**Following Up on Baseline Assessment:** TG p. D28<br>**Performance:** TG p. D28<br><br>**Chapter 1 Summative Assessment**<br>Reflect and Evaluate, p. D29<br>Chapter 1 Review/Test: AG pp. 87–88<br>*Science Notebook* pp. 171–172 |

TG= Teaching Guide   TRB= Teacher Resource Book   AG= Assessment Guide   *Materials in Equipment Kit

# CHAPTER 1
## Introducing the Chapter

# Chapter Overview

**Chapter Concept** Water, an essential natural resource, is found on Earth's surface, in the atmosphere, and underground.

## Theme: Systems

The water cycle is a system of processes that maintain Earth's water balance.

## Common Misconceptions

Students might think that people in other parts of the world obtain water as easily as they do. This chapter focuses on the fact that although water is common, only a small fraction of it is usable fresh water.

## Options for
# Setting the Stage

## Warm-Up Activity

Student pairs can make a list of all the ways their families use water. Make sure they include drinking, cooking, washing dishes, washing clothes, and so on. Students can brainstorm about which of the uses consumes more water and where the water they use comes from.

Use *Science Notebook* pp. 157–158.

## Discussion Starter:
### Florida's Precious Water

• **Suppose you could ask a water official only one question about the water used in your area. What would it be?** Students might ask about the sources of the water, how it is stored, and how it is distributed.

• **Career:** Science Writer
Explain to students that a science writer's task is to gather information from many sources, organize it, and communicate it to other people. A science writer's projects can include books, newspaper or magazine articles, or television and radio broadcasts. Science writers might have degrees in science, creative writing, journalism, or other fields.

---

# CHAPTER 1

# WATER, WATER, EVERYWHERE

Water has many uses. You drink it. You cook with it. You use it to wash dishes and clothes. Farmers depend on it to make their crops grow and to keep their animals healthy. Industry has many needs for it. Where do we get all this water?

### Florida's Precious Water

**N**icole Duplaix is a writer. She writes articles on science topics for magazines. One of her favorite topics is the huge swampy area in Florida called the Everglades.

The lakes and rivers of the Everglades supply water to homes, farms, and industries in southern Florida. As a science writer, Duplaix alerts people to things that are harming the area's water supply.

Duplaix interviews scientists and public officials who have ideas about how to protect the Everglades. Her articles help readers learn ways to protect this valuable water source.

Someday you might write a science article about the water supply in your area. What would you tell your readers?

D4

---

# Home-School Connection

The Explore at Home activity "The State of Things" encourages students to investigate the different states of water at home. Distribute the activity (TRB p. 16) when students have completed the chapter. Discuss which state of matter snow represents.

**Explore at Home**

Name _____ Date _____

## THE STATE OF THINGS

*Our science class has been studying Earth's water. We have been learning that water on Earth is found in three states—solid, liquid, and gas and is constantly changing state in the water cycle. You can explore the forms of water in the water cycle just by looking around your home.*

### Procedure

With a family member, make a list of the places where water can be found in and around your home. Decide whether this water is a solid, liquid, or gas. Liquid and solid water are easy to find. However, the gas state of water, water vapor, is invisible. You can't see water vapor, but you can see when water vapor condenses to liquid water. Look at the air over a pot of boiling water to see a small cloud. This is water vapor that condensed into tiny particles of liquid water. The small cloud quickly evaporates into the air, but if enough water vapor evaporates, it'll soon condense to liquid water on your windows. You can also see water vapor condense on mirrors when you bathe, or when you breathe on the mirror.

### Results

Was water most commonly found as a solid, liquid, or gas? Would your list be different at another time of year?

◀ The lakes and rivers of the Everglades supply water to people, as well as to wildlife, such as this roseate spoonbill.

D5

## Chapter Road Map

 **INVESTIGATION 1**

**Where Is Water Found on Earth and Why Is Water Important?**

| **Activities** | **Resources** |
| --- | --- |
| ✳ The Water Planet | ✳ A Watery World |
| Dry Up! | |

 **INVESTIGATION 2**

**How Does Nature Move Water?**

| **Activities** | **Resources** |
| --- | --- |
| Disappearing Act | ✳ Nature Recycles |
| ✳ Water Ups and Downs | The Salty Problem |

 **INVESTIGATION 3**

**Where Are Sources of Fresh Water Found?**

| **Activities** | **Resources** |
| --- | --- |
| Well, Well | Bring Water Home |
| ✳ Soak It Up! | ✳ Getting to the Source |

## ✳ Pressed for Time?

As you work through the upcoming investigations, focus on the activities and resources identified by the clock.

 Look for this symbol in front of questions that help develop Scientific Reasoning Skills.

## Technology Alert

 **CD-ROM**

**Water Everywhere** and **What Goes Around** Enhances or replaces Investigations 1, 2, and 3

**Water Everywhere** introduces the importance of Earth's fresh water. Students probe to discover how much of the water on Earth is actually drinkable. Students use the Rivers, Oceans, and Seas Data Pack and the Lakes Data Pack to record ways in which water is used and write about a day without water.

In **What Goes Around** students observe the water cycle and learn about its stages by clicking on labels and hearing audio clues. They drag labels to identify parts of the water cycle. When all the parts are labeled correctly, the animation begins.

# WHERE IS WATER FOUND ON EARTH AND WHY IS WATER IMPORTANT?

## Planner

**Subconcept** Water, which covers almost three-fourths of Earth's surface and is essential for sustaining life, is used by people in many ways.

### Objectives

• **Compare** the amount of land and water on Earth.

• **Infer** why water is important to living things.

• **Identify** the kind of water people need and how they use it.

**Pacing** 2–3 class periods

**Science Term** natural resource

## Activate Prior Knowledge

**Baseline Assessment** Ask: **Where is water found?** Make a class list and save it for use in Following Up.

# WHERE IS WATER FOUND ON EARTH AND WHY IS WATER IMPORTANT?

What makes Earth a great place to live? Water! Our planet is the only one that is known to have liquid water. In fact, Earth is sometimes called the water planet. You'll find out why as you investigate.

## Activity

### The Water Planet

*Which covers more of Earth's surface—land or water? In this activity you'll make an estimate of how much water covers Earth.*

**MATERIALS**
• metric ruler
• paper plate
• colored markers
• map of the world
• tracing paper
• scissors
• *Science Notebook*

**SAFETY**
Be careful when using scissors.

### Procedure

**1.** Using a ruler, draw two lines on a paper plate to make four equal sections as shown in the drawing. This is your pie graph.

**2.** Look at a map of the world. Talk with your group and estimate what part of Earth's surface is covered with water—$\frac{1}{4}$, $\frac{1}{2}$, or $\frac{3}{4}$. Record your estimate in your *Science Notebook*.

**3.** Color one or more sections of your pie graph to show your estimate.

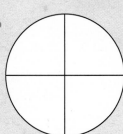

Step 1

D6

## Activity The Water Planet

**Preview** *Students should find that about three-fourths of Earth's surface is covered with water.*

### 1. Get Ready

**Time** 40 minutes

**Grouping** groups of 3–5

**Collaborative Strategy** Each group member can cut out parts of the map to make the land and water shapes.

**Materials Hints** Students may find it helpful to lay the cut-out shapes on graph paper, Use Activity Support Master "Graph Paper" (TRB p. 43). A map of the world can be found on Activity Support Master D1 (TRB p. 40).

## Responding to Individual Needs

**Visual/Spatial Activity** Allow students to examine a relief globe to aid them in visualizing and comparing the percentages of water and land on Earth. Point out the location of the major bodies of water and land features such as mountains, plains, and deserts. Invite students to touch the globe, tracing the land masses with their fingers. Discuss the colors used on the globe and what they represent.

Step 4

**4.** Now check your estimate. Lay tracing paper over a map of the world and then trace the water and land areas. Cut out the shapes. Write *water* on the pieces that are water and *land* on the pieces that are land.

**5.** Lay the cutouts of land and water on a table. Think of a way to arrange them to compare the amount of water to the amount of land. Record how you did it.

### Analyze and Conclude

**1.** Look at all the pie graphs made by your class. What fraction of water do most of the graphs show?

**2.** Compare your estimate with what you found in step 5.

**3.** Infer why Earth is called the water planet.

**INVESTIGATE FURTHER!**

**RESEARCH**

What fraction of your state is covered by water? Look at a map to help you make an estimate. Make a pie graph to show your estimate.

D7

---

## Investigate Further

### Research

Students should use a map of their state and follow the same procedure used in this activity to estimate what fraction of the state is water. Before students look at their state map, ask them to predict what fraction of the state is water. Students may need guidance in making their predictions. Ask them if the fraction will be less than $\frac{1}{2}$. If they say yes, ask if the fraction will be less than $\frac{1}{3}$. Continue in this way, asking students about progressively smaller fractions ($\frac{1}{3}$, $\frac{1}{4}$, $\frac{1}{8}$, and so on). After students have made their pie graphs, check their graphs to see that they have used numbers correctly to represent the portion of their state covered with water and to see that they have correctly interpreted the data as a fraction. Have students use *Science Notebook* p. 160 for their pie graphs.

---

## 2. Guide the Procedure

- Have students use paper clips to secure the tracing paper to their world maps.
- To aid students in arranging their land and water cutouts, ask: **How can you make the pieces fit together?** Move them around to eliminate unwanted empty space.

 **How did cutting apart the map and rearranging the pieces help you check the estimate shown in your graph?** Responses may include that cutting apart the map and rearranging the pieces provided another way to look at the data being analyzed in addition to providing a method for verifying its accuracy.

Have students record their estimates and answer questions on *Science Notebook* p. 159.

You may wish to have students use the CD-ROM Writer to organize and display their data.

## 3. Assess Performance

### Process Skills Checklist

- Did students use numbers correctly to **estimate** the portion of the Earth covered with water? Did they understand the meaning of fractions and **apply** them to the activity?
- Did students **infer** why Earth is called the water planet? Was the inference based on **evaluating** activity results showing that most of Earth's surface is covered with water?

### Analyze and Conclude

**1.** Most of the pie graphs should show three-fourths of Earth covered by water.

**2.** The estimates should compare well because students based them on a world map. The cutouts helped students check their estimates.

**3.** Students may infer that Earth is called the water planet because most of it is covered with water.

# Activity 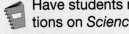 Dry Up!

**Preview** *Students demonstrate the presence of water in a carrot by showing that the mass a slice of dry carrot is less than the mass of a slice of fresh carrot.*

**Advance Preparation** *See p. D4b.*

## 1. Get Ready

**Time** about 20 minutes the first day; 5 minutes the second day; 20 minutes the third day

**Grouping** pairs

**Multi-Age Strategy** Students who are familiar with measuring mass can assist other students.

## 2. Guide the Procedure

 Encourage predictions by asking: **What do you think will happen to the carrot slice in a sunny, dry place?** Most likely students will think the carrot slice will shrink and shrivel a bit.

Have students record their data and answer questions on *Science Notebook* p. 161.

You may wish to have students use the CD-ROM Spreadsheet to organize and display their data in a chart.

## 3. Assess Performance

### Process Skills Checklist

- Did students **measure** and **record** the mass of a carrot slice correctly when it was fresh and again after it dried out?

- Did students **infer** that a decrease in water caused the differences in the mass of the carrot slice?

- Did students **infer** the presence of water in human beings based on the information they gathered?

### Analyze and Conclude

1. The change in mass is due to the loss of water.

2. Students may infer that since carrots are largely water, it is likely that water makes up part of other plants. They may also reason that because plants must be watered to survive, it is likely that other plants contain water.

3. Since plants are living things, students might infer that animals, including humans, also contain water. Students may also infer that since they drink water, human beings must contain water.

---

# Activity

**MATERIALS**
- carrot slice
- balance and masses
- pie pan
- *Science Notebook*

## Dry Up!

*A carrot is a living thing. Does a carrot have water in it? You'll find out by doing this activity.*

### Procedure

**1.** Use a balance to measure the mass of a carrot slice. Record its mass in your *Science Notebook*.

**2.** Place the carrot slice in a pie pan.

**3.** Put the pan in a sunny, dry place for one day.

**4.** The next day, turn the carrot slice over. Let it remain in the sun for another day.

**5.** The following day, again measure the mass of the carrot slice. Record your result.

Step 1

### Analyze and Conclude

**1.** Compare the mass of the carrot in steps 1 and 5. What can you infer caused the difference?

**2.** A carrot is a plant. Make an inference about whether there is water in other plants. Give reasons for your inference.

**3.** Infer whether there is water in human beings. Explain your reasoning.

D8

---

 **Responding to Individual Needs**

**Students Acquiring English** Encourage students to write short descriptions of the carrot slice before and after they allow it to dry out. Prompt them to use descriptive words for its shape, color, and texture before it is dried. They can use comparative forms (less moist, drier, and so on) of the same words to describe the carrot slice after it dries. Before they begin to write, you might help them to develop a list of words that could be used in their descriptions.

Have students use the CD-ROM Writer to write their descriptions.

# A Watery World

We live in a watery world. Think back to the activity on pages D6 and D7. You found out that Earth is covered by more water than land. In fact, about three fourths of Earth is covered by water.

**Water on Earth**

Pretend that all the water on Earth could be poured into 100 cups. Of the 100 cups, 97 would be filled with salt water, water that contains salt. Most of this salt is table salt, the kind used to flavor food. The salt comes from rocks and soil carried by rivers and streams into the ocean. Because of the large amount of salt, you'd become sick, or even die, if you drank a lot of sea water. Your body cannot use salt water for its functions.

If 97 of the 100 cups contain salt water, that leaves 3 cups of fresh water. Fresh water is water that people and animals can drink. But of these three cups of water, two are frozen into ice. These two cups of ice represent water frozen in icecaps, glaciers, and icebergs. That leaves only one cup of fresh water for all the living things on Earth to use.

## EARTH'S WATER

97 cups salt water

Ice    Liquid

3 cups fresh water

**D9**

## Integrating the Curriculum

### Science & Math

FRACTIONS  **What to Do** Help students visualize what fraction of Earth's water is fresh and what fraction is salty based on the comparisons given on page D9 in their book. Instead of using cups, have them count out 100 counters to represent the total amount of water on Earth. They should make ten groups of counters, ten counters per group.

**What's the Result?** Have students arrange counters to show what fraction of all Earth's water is fresh (3/100) and record their findings on paper. Then have them show what fraction of Earth's water is salty. (97/100)

**Multi-Age Classroom** Students can work in small groups to do this activity. They can consult each other.

---

# A Watery World

**Preview** *Students come to understand that they need fresh water to drink and to carry out many functions in their lives. A very small percentage of Earth's water is liquid fresh water.*

## 1. Get Ready

### Science Term  natural resource

### Background

• Water heats up more slowly than most other substances and holds its heat longer. The water contained in some living things known as warm-blooded, or endothermic, animals allows these animals to keep their internal temperature relatively constant. These living things may also use some of their water content to get rid of excess heat as perspiration which carries heat away from the body.

### Discussion Starter

**If so much of the Earth's surface is covered with water, why are there places in the world where drinking water is hard to find?** Most of Earth's water is salt water that is not usable for drinking, washing, farming, and industrial uses. Also, fresh water is not distributed evenly around the world. Freshwater lakes, rivers, and underground aquifers vary greatly in their abundance from place to place. In addition, much of the Earth's fresh water is polluted, or unfit for use by living things.

## 2. Guide the Discussion

*Choose from the following strategies to facilitate discussion.*

### Connecting to the Activities

• *Dry Up!, p. D8*
  **How did the carrot slice look after it lost its water?** The carrot slice was shriveled and looked dried up.

• **What do you think would happen to a carrot plant if it lost all of its water?** Students may respond that since a carrot plant is a living thing, without water, the carrot plant would die.

## Making Comparisons

• **How is the water in the ocean different from the water that comes from the faucet?** Students will most likely say that the water in the ocean contains a lot of salt. They might also mention that the tap water is cleaner.

## Making Inferences

 **Do you think fresh water is a valuable resource? Why?** Students will likely consider fresh water valuable because people need it to live. It is also needed for industrial purposes, farming, and other uses.

## Thinking Critically

• **Suppose a ship you are on has engine trouble. You start to get into a small rescue boat carrying a jug of water and a loaf of bread. You are told you can take only one of these things. Which should you take?** Students should choose the water since living things can live longer without food than without water.

### Responding to Individual Needs

**Students Acquiring English** Have students search in old magazines for illustrations showing ways in which people use water. They can cut out and arrange the pictures to make a water-usage collage.

## 3. Assess Understanding

Ask students to work in pairs or groups of three to make a pie graph to illustrate what they have learned. The pie graph should show the fraction of Earth covered by salt water, liquid fresh water, and frozen fresh water. Tell students to be sure to label the graph clearly.

▲ From space, Earth looks blue because of all the water.

Water is the most common substance on Earth. But large bodies of water such as oceans and rivers are not the only places water is found. When you did the activity on page D8, you found out that a carrot has a lot of water in it. In fact, *all* living things contain a large amount of water. Nearly two thirds of your body is water. Look at the drawing below. How much water makes up an elephant, a potato, and a tomato?

**Using Water**

Like air and soil, water is a natural resource. A **natural resource** is a useful material from Earth. All living things need water to stay alive. A healthy person might live for more than a month without food, but the same person could survive only about three days without water.

While you need water just to survive, you use water in many different ways. Look at the pictures on the next page to see some uses of water.

WATER IN LIVING THINGS

$\frac{3}{4}$ Water

$\frac{2}{3}$ Water

$\frac{4}{5}$ Water

$\frac{9}{10}$ Water

**D10**

## Investigate Further

### Integrating the Sciences

LIFE SCIENCE **What to Do** Show students two identical plants. Have students water them with equal amounts of water: one with salt water and one with fresh water. In all other ways, the plants should receive the same treatment: the same amount of sunlight, soil, and the same temperature. Remind students to record their data, including measurements of growth and other observations.

**What's the Result?** After about a week, students may notice that the plants watered with salt water wilt and die. Encourage students to share and compare their results with other groups.

## WATER USES IN THE UNITED STATES

▲ **INDUSTRY** Water is used as a source of power and to make many products. This machine is cooled by water.

**HOMES** You use water every day. You use water when you bathe, cook, clean, and water plants. ▼

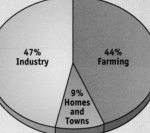

Pie chart:
- 47% Industry
- 44% Farming
- 9% Homes and Towns

▲ **FARMING** Water is used for livestock and to grow crops. In dry places, farmers must irrigate their fields.

**TOWNS** Water is used to put out fires, treat sewage, and clean streets. ▼

### ——— INVESTIGATION 1 ———

**1.** Earth is called the water planet, yet finding enough drinking water for everyone on the planet is sometimes a problem. Explain why.

**2.** Pretend you are a water-use detective. List four ways that people use water. Why is water so important?

**D11**

## Assessment

### Portfolio

**Individual** Ask students to write a paragraph that explains why Earth's fresh water should be used wisely. Encourage them to suggest some ways they can use water more wisely.

Have students use the CD-ROM Writer to write their paragraphs.

**Investigation Review**
*Where Is Water Found on Earth and Why Is Water Important?*

Name _____ Date _____

**1. a.** Shade the part of the graph that shows how much of Earth's water is salt water.

**b.** What does the unshaded part of the graph represent?

how much of Earth's water is fresh water

**c.** Draw a pie graph to show how much of Earth's surface is water and how much is land. Shade in the part of your pie graph that shows how much of Earth's surface is water.

**2.** Use the words in the box to complete the puzzle.

glaciers   living things   resources   salt   survive   water

**Across**
**2.** All living things need water to ___.
**4.** Earth is sometimes called the ___ planet.
**5.** I make food tasty, but I make water unfit to drink. I am ___.

**Down**
**1.** Air, soil, and water are natural ___.
**3.** Most of Earth's fresh water is frozen in icecaps, ___, and icebergs.
**6.** All ___ contain water.

Answers will vary. Students should be able to make the connection between the water on a planet and its ability to sustain life. Since other planets, such as Mars, do not have liquid water, they are not likely to support plants and animals.

**Process Skills**
**Communicating** Earth is the only planet known to have liquid water and all living things need water. Is it likely that other planets, such as Mars, have life? Explain your answer on a separate sheet of paper.

## Close the Investigation

### Critical Thinking Skills
**Analyzing, Expressing Ideas, Solving Problems**

**1.** Even though three-fourths of Earth is covered by water, most of the water is salt water. Most of the world's fresh water is frozen in ice caps and glaciers. Therefore, drinking water can be scarce in certain places.

**2.** People use water for drinking, personal cleanliness, cooking and cleaning, growing plants, producing power, cooling machines, mining, manufacturing, and so on. Water is important because it is necessary for people to survive and for its other uses.

**Challenge** Ask students to use a map to find places in the United States and the rest of the world where getting enough fresh water might be a problem. Students should look for places that have a lack of freshwater lakes and rivers, such as the American Southwest, and desert areas around the world.

### Following Up

**Baseline Assessment** Return to the list the class made of where water is found. Have students change or add to the list as necessary. Point out how the list has changed as they have learned new information. Relate this to how ideas in science change as people learn more information.

**Reteaching** Have students return to the idea that freshwater rivers flowing into oceans carry salt from the land to the ocean. Let them work in small groups to find on a map large rivers of North America. Ask them to trace where these rivers begin and where they empty into the ocean. Suggest that they make a chart listing at least four rivers and the ocean or gulf into which each flows.

 Use *Science Notebook* p. 162.

◀ **Investigation Review**
Use Investigation Review p. 84 in the *Assessment Guide*.

# HOW DOES NATURE MOVE WATER?

## Planner

**Subconcept** As water moves through the water cycle, it changes state as heat energy is added or taken away.

### Objectives

- **Describe** the relationships between evaporation, condensation, and precipitation in the water cycle.
- **Explain** the process of desalination.

**Pacing** 2–3 class periods

**Science Terms** liquid, solid, gas, evaporate, water vapor, precipitation, condense, water cycle

## Activate Prior Knowledge

**Baseline Assessment** Have students draw a picture or write a paragraph describing what happens to a raindrop from the time it falls from the sky to the time it returns to the air. Save these materials for use in Following Up.

---

## INVESTIGATION 2

# HOW DOES NATURE MOVE WATER?

Think about this: If all water runs downhill to the ocean, why doesn't the ocean overflow? You'll find out where the water goes in this investigation.

# Activity

## Disappearing Act

*Water disappears from an uncovered cup. How does temperature affect this change?*

**MATERIALS**
- metric measuring cup
- water
- 2 plastic cups
- grease pencil
- *Science Notebook*

**SAFETY**
Clean up any spills immediately.

### Procedure

Pour 100 mL of water into two plastic cups. Mark the level of the water on each with a grease pencil. Put one cup in a warm place and the other in a cool place. With your group, **predict** in which cup the water level will change the most. **Record** your prediction in your *Science Notebook*. After two days, **record** your observations.

### Analyze and Conclude

**1.** How did the amount of water in the cups differ after two days? **Compare** this to your prediction.

**2.** **Hypothesize** what happened in this activity.

D12

---

# Activity Disappearing Act

**Preview** *Students find that water evaporates more quickly in a warm place than a cool place.*

## 1. Get Ready

**Time** 10 minutes the first day; 10 minutes the second day

**Grouping** groups of 3–4

**Collaborative Strategy** Together students could fill cups, mark cups, and discuss their predictions and observations.

**Safety** Review safety precautions with students.

## 2. Guide the Procedure

- **What would be a good place for each cup?** Warm places: shelf or counter in the sunlight. Cool places: shady spots or closets.

---

Have students record their data and answer questions on *Science Notebook* p. 163.

You may wish to have students use the CD-ROM Spreadsheet to organize and display their data.

## 3. Assess Performance

### Process Skills Checklist
- Did students correctly **record** the requested data?
- Did students' **hypotheses** explain the changes observed?

### Analyze and Conclude
**1.** Both cups had lower water levels but that the water level was lower in the cup placed in the warmer area.

**2.** A warmer temperature causes more water to disappear than a cooler temperature does.

# Activity

## Water Ups and Downs

*Liquid water disappears from a cup and goes into the air. Find out how you can get the liquid water back again.*

### Procedure

**1.** Mold a pan-shaped cover from aluminum foil for a plastic jar. Make sure the cover fits tightly over the jar's opening.

**2.** Remove the foil cover and place it off to one side.

**3.** Now have your teacher add hot tap water to the jar until it is one-third full.

**4.** Put the foil cover back on the jar. Secure the cover with a rubber band. Quickly place a few ice cubes in the foil cover. Watch closely! **Observe** what happens on the underside of the foil. **Record** your observations in your *Science Notebook*.

Step 4

### Analyze and Conclude

**1.** You've **made a model** of Earth. The warm water represents a lake or an ocean. The air above it represents the air around Earth. The air high above Earth is cold. The ice on the foil cover cooled the air higher in the jar. Based on your observations of your model, **hypothesize** how water gets into the air.

**2.** **Infer** whether water on Earth might go into the air faster during the day or at night. Explain why you think so.

D13

---

 **Responding to Individual Needs**

**Visual Spatial Activity** Invite students to make a diagram of what happened in the activity. They should label the materials they used (jar, foil cover, water, ice) and draw what they observed. Have them prepare a second drawing that includes a body of water and air above it. This drawing can be labeled to show how water moves into Earth's air.

Have students use the CD-ROM Painter and Writer to draw and label their diagrams.

---

# Activity Water Ups and Downs

**Preview** *Students should observe that liquid water changes to water vapor when warmed, then changes back to a liquid when cooled.*

## 1. Get Ready

**Time** about 30 minutes

**Grouping** groups of 3–4

**Collaborative Strategy** One group member may record the observations, while others express the observations verbally.

**Safety** Review safety precautions with students.

## 2. Guide the Procedure

Encourage students to make predictions. Ask: **What do you think will happen after ice cubes are placed in the foil cover? Why do you think so?** Accept all answers that are based on a prior knowledge of the process of condensation.

- Alert students that they must be ready to observe any changes immediately, since not much time passes between changes.

Have students record their observations and answer questions on *Science Notebook* p. 164.

You may wish to have students use the CD-ROM Writer to record their data.

## 3. Assess Performance

### Process Skills Checklist
- Did students **record** their observations clearly? Were they able to **communicate** the presence of moisture on the underside of the foil?
- Did students make a reasonable **hypothesis?** Was it based on their observations?

### Analyze and Conclude
1. Students should hypothesize that water gets into the air through evaporation.
2. Students may infer that evaporation occurs faster during the day because of the sun's heat. This inference should be based on the warm water in the jar, which represents a lake or ocean warmed by the Sun.

# Nature Recycles

**Preview** *Students focus on water in its three states and nature's ability to recycle water from one state to another.*

## 1. Get Ready

### Science Terms
liquid, solid, gas, evaporate, water vapor, precipitation, condense, water cycle

### Background

- Another source of water vapor in the atmosphere is transpiration, the process by which plants release water vapor into the atmosphere through their leaves. Water molecules evaporate into the air from openings in the leaf. As the water evaporates, it creates a suction force behind the openings in the leaf. This force causes more water to rise in the plant's tubes to take the place of the evaporated water. On a warm day the process speeds up. Places where large numbers of trees are cut down become drier, sometimes desert-like, because transpiration no longer adds needed water to the atmosphere.

### Discussion Starter

- **If you leave a boiling kettle of water on a stove, what eventually happens to the water?** Students may respond that it "disappears" into the air.

- **If you leave a glass of ice water sitting on a table on a hot, humid day, water droplets form on the outside of the glass. Where do these water droplets come from?** Students may say that the water droplets came from water vapor in the air, which was cooled by the ice.

# Nature Recycles

What constantly changes yet always stays the same? If you don't know, you're about to find out!

Think back to the last time you had a drink of water. Some of that water could have been the same water a dinosaur drank! The same amount of water has been on Earth for millions of years. But the form, or state, of water is always changing.

### States of Matter

Water, like all the things around you, is matter. Air, milk, books—all are matter. And matter exists in one of three basic states—as a liquid, a solid, or a gas.

A **liquid** has no definite shape, but it takes up a definite amount of space. Look at the pictures below. The colored water takes up space, but it doesn't have a particular shape. It takes the shape of the container that holds it. All liquids do this.

A **solid** has a definite shape and takes up a definite amount of space. You know that you can't "pour" a sneaker into a jar. This is because solids can't change shape.

A **gas** is a state of matter that has no definite shape and takes up no definite amount of space. A gas spreads out to fill the container that holds it, and the space a gas takes up varies with the size of the container.

**How are liquids and solids different?** ▼

D14

## Investigate Further

### Cultural Connection

**What You Need** 5 lbs. crushed ice, bucket, fruit juice (other than citrus) in a plastic container with lid

**What to Do** Have students make water ices. Explain that, in his travels to China in the 1200s, Marco Polo learned about water ices. Place ice in the bucket and sprinkle with some salt. Set the container of juice on the ice. Surround it with the remaining ice and salt. Turn the container slowly for several minutes.

**What's the Result? What happens to the juice?** It should freeze in about 30 minutes. **What does salt do to ice?** The ice melts. **If salt water has a lower freezing point than fresh water, why does the juice freeze as the ice melts?** The salt lowers the temperature of the ice/water mixture below the freezing point of water, which freezes the juice.

You might have seen someone inflating a helium (hē′lē əm) balloon. Helium is a kind of gas. When helium or any gas is released into a balloon, it spreads out and fills the entire balloon, as you can see in the drawing to the right.

**Amazing Water**

Water is the only substance that can be found in nature as a solid, a liquid, and a gas. How can you change the state of water? Think about the activity on page D12 in which you placed water in a warm place. You saw that it seemed to disappear faster than water in a cooler place. But the water didn't really disappear. It changed state. The water changed from a liquid to a gas. When liquid water changes to a gas, that water is said to **evaporate** (ē vap′ə rāt).

To change the state of water, you have to add or take away heat energy. If you put water in a freezer, the water turns to a solid called ice. The freezer *takes away* heat energy from the water.

When you boil water, you are *adding* heat energy to water. Heating changes liquid water to a gas. When water is a gas, it is called **water vapor**. You can't see water vapor, but there are times when you can feel it. On some warm days in summer, the air seems heavy and wet and your skin feels "sticky." On such days there's a lot of water vapor in the air. When the air feels cool and dry, there is less water vapor in the air.

To change the state of water, you have to add or take away heat energy. ▼

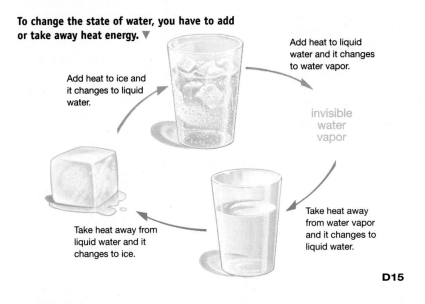

Add heat to liquid water and it changes to water vapor.

Add heat to ice and it changes to liquid water.

invisible water vapor

Take heat away from liquid water and it changes to ice.

Take heat away from water vapor and it changes to liquid water.

D15

## Science, Technology & Society

**What to Do** Encourage students to find out about dry ice. **What is it?** Solid carbon dioxide **How cold is it?** -78.5°C (-109.3°F) **How is dry ice different from ice made from water?** Dry ice is a substance that changes from a solid to a gas without first becoming a liquid. **What is dry ice used for?** Refrigeration, medicine **What is dangerous about dry ice?** It is so much colder than ice made from water (0°C, 32°F) it could cause frostbite to people handling it.
**Multi-Age Classroom** Let students work in groups. Older students can research while younger students can help share the results with the class.

# 2. Guide the Discussion

*Choose from the following strategies to facilitate discussion.*

## Making Inferences

- **What examples of matter are present in your classroom?** Whatever students name in the classroom will be matter. **Is air an example of matter? Why?** Students should infer that even invisible things, such as gases in air, are matter because they have mass and take up space. If students don't think air has mass, have them compare the mass of a deflated basketball with the mass of a basketball filled with air.

## Connecting to the Activities

- *Disappearing Act, p. D12*
  **In the activity, more water disappeared from one cup than from the other. What caused this to happen?** More heat energy was added to one cup than the other.

- *Water Ups and Downs, p. D13*
  **In the activity, was heat added or taken away from water vapor to cause it to condense on the foil cover?** Heat was taken away to cause water vapor to condense.

  **What would you need to do to the liquid water to change it to a solid state?** More heat energy would have to be taken away from the water.

## Thinking About the Data

- Draw students' attention to the diagram at the bottom of p. D15. Then ask: **When something cools, is heat energy being added to or taken away from it?** Taken away **When something heats up, is heat energy being added to or taken away from it?** Added **How does liquid water change if you take away enough heat energy?** It becomes solid (ice). **Is heat energy added to or taken away from liquid water as it turns into water vapor?** Added

## Drawing Conclusions

- **What evidence can you use to explain why the "cloud" over a boiling pot of water *is not* water vapor?** Students may state that water vapor is invisible. Thus, what they see cannot be water vapor. Tell them that the "cloud" they see is water vapor that has already condensed, or cooled enough to turn back into tiny droplets of water. The vapor is a thin invisible layer between the bubbling water and the "cloud." Water vapor is also in the air.

## Making Comparisons

 **Think again about the pan of boiling water. How is the "cloud" over that pan like a cloud in the sky?** Both are the result of water vapor that has condensed.

## Thinking Critically

**The water you drink today might have been part of a cloud two weeks ago. What makes this possible?** Accept answers that show an understanding of the water cycle.

## Drawing Conclusions

**Do you think the four captions in the drawing should be numbered? Where would you start numbering them? Would it be wrong to start in any other place?** If students think the captions should be numbered, let them suggest a starting point. They might start in the upper left-hand corner, following the way they would read. Let students suggest other starting points. At each starting point, follow the cycle through with the class. Students should conclude that the water cycle, like most cycles, has no true starting point.

To reinforce students' understanding of the water cycle, use **Transparency 18,** "The Water Cycle."

## THE WATER CYCLE

**PRECIPITATION** When water drops in clouds get bigger, they become heavy and fall to Earth as rain. If the air is cold enough, the drops may form hail, sleet, or snow. The liquid or solid forms of water that fall to Earth are kinds of **precipitation** (prē sip ə tā′shən).

**WATER ON THE GROUND** Some water from rainfall soaks into the ground. Some flows downhill and collects in lakes, rivers, and oceans. Some falls directly into these bodies of water.

When you add ice to a glass of lemonade, droplets of water often form on the outside of the glass. Water vapor in the air near the cold glass loses heat energy as the water vapor comes into contact with the cold glass. The water vapor changes to liquid water on the glass. When water vapor changes to liquid water, it is said to **condense**. In the activity on page D13, you saw water condense on the underside of the aluminum foil. How did the ice cubes on top of the foil help water condense?

### A Never-Ending Cycle

Remember the riddle that appeared on page D14? It asked, "What constantly changes yet always stays the same?" Do you know the answer yet?

It's water! The "constant changes" referred to in this riddle are changes in the state of water. These changes are part of something called the water cycle. The **water cycle** is the path that water follows as it evaporates into the air, condenses into clouds, and returns to Earth as rain.

Look at the drawing of the water cycle. Why is this path called a cycle? As you look at the picture, read what is happening in the different parts of the water cycle.

You've seen how water constantly changes. Water—that amazing substance—can change from a solid to a liquid to a gas and back again. Yet it always stays the same. No matter how often it changes from one state to another, water remains water.

**D16**

## Investigate Further

### Integrating the Sciences

**LIFE SCIENCE**

**What to Do** Students can demonstrate evaporation and condensation of moisture from a houseplant. Place a plastic bag over a small houseplant, securing the bag to the plant's stem with a rubber band. Place the plant in its bag in a location that receives strong sunlight. Let students check the bag every hour.
**What's the Result?** As the bag gets cloudy, ask: **What's happening?** Students should conclude that living things give off water vapor. The water vapor condenses on the bag, which is surrounded by cooler air.
**Multi-Age Classroom** Have the students work together in pairs to do the activity. One student can observe and describe what is happening while the other student records the information.

**WATER CONDENSES** When water vapor in the air cools, it condenses back into tiny droplets of liquid water. When there are many droplets together, they form clouds.

**WATER EVAPORATES** The sun warms the water. The heat energy causes water to evaporate and rise into the air as invisible water vapor.

# Integrating the Curriculum

## Science & the Arts

CARTOONING

**What to Do** Students can draw cartoons to show each part of the water cycle in their own region for a particular time of year. For example, the water cycle in the Midwest in winter would likely include snow. Then students could draw people wearing snow gear. They should give their drawing a title and label all the parts of the cycle.

**What's the Result?  In what area might the cycle you drew take place?** Students' drawings should reflect an understanding of the water cycle that can occur in the region they selected. For example, a cycle that shows people dressed in snow gear might be titled Wisconsin's Winter Water Cycle.

Have students use the CD-ROM Painter and Writer to draw and label their watercycle cartoons.

## SCIENCE IN LITERATURE

*Cloudy with a Chance of Meatballs*
by Judi Barrett
Students could substitute food choices of their own for the parts of the water cycle. Then they could write their own version of Chewandswallow weather.

## Responding to Individual Needs

**Students Acquiring English** As you point to a part of the water cycle, have a student describe what is happening in English. Record the description. Then assist the student in reading it to you.

## 3. Assess Understanding

Students can work in groups of three or four. Invite each group to role-play what happens during the water cycle. They can make paper signs to indicate what part of the cycle they are playing. They can use a narrator to describe the cycle.

RESOURCE

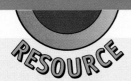

# The Salty Problem

**Preview** *Students focus on the problem of how to make fresh water from salt water.*

## 1. Get Ready

### Discussion Starter

**How might you try to obtain fresh water from ocean water?** Students may say that they would try a plan that imitates the natural water cycle.

## 2. Guide the Discussion

*Choose from the following strategies to facilitate discussion.*

### Connecting to the Activities

- ***Water Ups and Downs, p. D13***

**How does nature change water to desalinate it?** The sun heats ocean water. The water evaporates, leaving the salt behind. Water vapor that cools in the air condenses and falls to Earth as freshwater rain.

### Responding to Individual Needs

**Students Acquiring English** Have students describe in English what is happening in each step of the diagram.

### Making Comparisons

- **What parts of nature's desalination process might you use to obtain fresh water?** Students might respond that they could heat water, changing it to a vapor, then let it cool and condense it to form fresh water.

### Identifying and Solving Problems

- **Why is desalination expensive?** Whenever you heat something, you need energy which can be costly.

## 3. Assess Understanding

Ask students to describe how the activity Water Ups and Downs on p. D13 is similar to the desalination process. **What would you have to add to the activity setup to make it a miniature desalination plant?** A method of collecting the water that condenses on the foil

RESOURCE

# The Salty Problem

STS SCIENCE TECHNOLOGY & SOCIETY

What if the rain stopped and never fell again? You can imagine how dry everything would be. Suppose rainwater was your only source of fresh water. If it never rained, you would have quite a problem, wouldn't you?

Look at the map. Cape Verde, a group of islands off the western coast of Africa, has had almost no rain since 1968! That's long before you were born. So where do the people of Cape Verde find fresh water to drink?

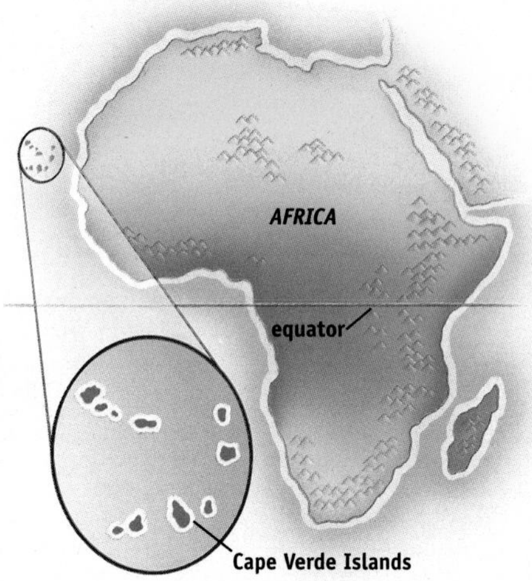


▲ Rainfall is scarce in Cape Verde.

### Fresh Water From Salt Water

Many islands, like the ones of Cape Verde, often don't have sources of fresh water. But they are surrounded by oceans, which are salt water. You know that people can't drink salt water without becoming ill. But can it be used as a source of fresh water?

Think about the water cycle. When salt water evaporates, only the water changes into water vapor, not the salt. Evaporation of salt water is part of the process of desalination (dē sal ə nā′shən). In desalination, salt is removed from ocean water to produce fresh water. One way this can be done is shown in the drawing on the next page.

It's very costly to desalinate ocean water. It takes a great deal of energy to pump the water through pipes and to heat it. But people who live on islands are happy to have fresh water—even if they must pay a lot in order to have it!

D18

## Investigate Further

### STS Science, Technology & Society

MAKING MODELS

**What to Do** Encourage groups of students to make the miniature desalination plant discussed in the section Assess Understanding. Have students repeat the activity on p. D13, but this time they should devise a way of collecting the water that condenses on the inside of the aluminum foil. Students should use salt water instead of fresh water.

**What's the Result?** Have students share their efforts—successes, partial successes, and failures—with the class. Point out that learning what doesn't work is valuable information in the search for finding out what *does* work.

## DESALINATION

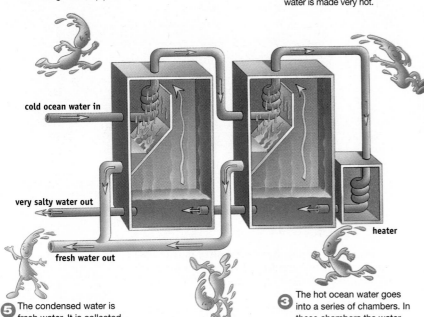

**1** Cold ocean water is pumped through coiled pipes.

**2** The ocean water in the pipes goes to a heater, where the water is made very hot.

cold ocean water in

very salty water out

fresh water out

heater

**5** The condensed water is fresh water. It is collected and moved to storage tanks. Then the water is piped to people's homes.

**4** The water vapor moves to cold, coiled pipes, where it condenses.

**3** The hot ocean water goes into a series of chambers. In these chambers the water quickly evaporates and turns to water vapor. Very salty water is left behind.

### INVESTIGATION 2

**1.** If water runs downhill to the oceans, why don't oceans overflow?

**2.** Draw a picture of the water cycle. Then explain the changes a drop of water goes through as it moves through the cycle.

D19

---

## Assessment

### Performance

**Debate** Have students pretend they live near the ocean in a community that has suffered from a lengthy drought. They must decide whether or not to build an expensive desalination plant. If they build it, students must decide how they will pay for it. As students discuss the problem, encourage them to give reasons for thinking as they do.

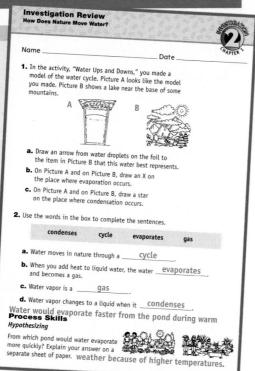

**Investigation Review**
**How Does Nature Move Water?**

Name _____  Date _____

**1.** In the activity, "Water Ups and Downs," you made a model of the water cycle. Picture A looks like the model you made. Picture B shows a lake near the base of some mountains.

A          B

**a.** Draw an arrow from water droplets on the foil to the item in Picture B that this water best represents.

**b.** On Picture A and on Picture B, draw an X on the place where evaporation occurs.

**c.** On Picture A and on Picture B, draw a star on the place where condensation occurs.

**2.** Use the words in the box to complete the sentences.

| condenses | cycle | evaporates | gas |

**a.** Water moves in nature through a ___cycle___.

**b.** When you add heat to liquid water, the water ___evaporates___ and becomes a gas.

**c.** Water vapor is a ___gas___.

**d.** Water vapor changes to a liquid when it ___condenses___.

**Process Skills** Water would evaporate faster from the pond during warm
*Hypothesizing*

From which pond would water evaporate more quickly? Explain your answer on a separate sheet of paper. weather because of higher temperatures.

---

## Close the Investigation

 **Critical Thinking Skills**
Synthesizing, Expressing Ideas, Solving Problems

**1.** The processes of evaporation and condensation which occur during the water cycle keep the ocean from overflowing.

**2.** Students' drawings should include the following ideas: Energy from the Sun makes some of the water in a body of water evaporate to form water vapor. Some of the water vapor condenses to form a cloud. In time water droplets in the cloud get larger, then fall to Earth as precipitation. Then the cycle repeats.

**Challenge** Have students find examples of evaporation and condensation that occur in their homes or in a car or bus. Some examples are: the cycle that occurs when they take a warm shower (the air gets humid, the mirror fogs up and drops of water run down), and the windows of the car or bus fog up on a cold day and drops run down the cold glass.

### Following Up

**Baseline Assessment** Return to the students' drawings and paragraphs describing what happens to a raindrop after it falls from the sky. Have them correct or elaborate on their work as necessary. Ask them to explain how their ideas changed as they learned new information.

**Reteaching** Prepare sentence strips describing the parts of the water cycle. Attach them to a bulletin board in random order. Have students rearrange the strips into the correct order to show the complete water cycle.

 To reinforce students' understanding of desalination, you may use **Transparency 19**, "Desalination."

 Use *Science Notebook* p. 165.

### ◄ Investigation Review
Use Investigation Review p. 85 in the *Assessment Guide*.

# WHERE ARE SOURCES OF FRESH WATER FOUND?

## Planner

**Subconcept** Our freshwater supplies come from surface water and ground water.

**Objectives**

- **Make a model** of a well.
- **Measure** the amount of water that passes through gravel, sand, and soil.
- **Describe** examples of places where getting fresh water cannot be taken for granted.
- **Explain** how many cities get their fresh water from rivers, lakes, and wells.

**Pacing** 3–4 class periods

**Science Terms** surface water, reservoir, ground water, aquifer

## Activate Prior Knowledge

**Baseline Assessment** Ask: **Where do people get their drinking water?** List as many sources as students can name. Save for use in Following Up.

## Activity Well, Well

**Preview** *Students focus on how a well works and should find that water rises in their models of a well.*

### 1. Get Ready

**Time** about 30 minutes

**Grouping** groups of 3–4

**Collaborative Strategy** One student can complete steps 1 and 2. Another student can pour the water in step 3. Other students should observe and record the results.

**Materials Hints** Make sure students start with dry sand.

**Safety** Review safety precautions with students.

---

# WHERE ARE SOURCES OF FRESH WATER FOUND?

INVESTIGATION ③

Rain, snow, and other forms of precipitation bring fresh water to Earth. But how do we get fresh water where and when we need it? In this investigation you'll find out.

## Activity

### Well, Well

*In many places the ground holds water like a sponge. In this activity, find out about one way people get that fresh water out of the ground.*

**Procedure**

**1.** Fill a small pie pan nearly to its top with sand.

**2.** Push a plastic cup, from which the bottom part has been cut off, into the sand. Use a plastic spoon to scoop the sand out of the cup. You've made a model of a well.

Step 2

D20

**MATERIALS**
- goggles
- small pie pan
- sand
- small soft-plastic cup with the bottom cut off
- plastic spoon
- water
- timer
- *Science Notebook*

**SAFETY**

Wear goggles during this activity. Clean up any spills immediately.

---

## Responding to Individual Needs

**Students Acquiring English** When they answer question 4 in Analyze and Conclude, suggest that students draw a diagram to show what they predict will happen to a well if it doesn't rain for a few days. Have them label their diagrams in their native language and in English.

Have students use the CD-ROM Painter and Writer to draw and label their diagrams.

Step 4

**3.** With your group, **predict** what will happen when you add water to the sand around the cup. **Record** your prediction in your *Science Notebook*.

**4.** Pour enough water into the sand around the well to soak the sand. Wait about five minutes and then look into your well. **Record** your observations.

### Analyze and Conclude

**1.** In step 4, what did you see in the well?

**2.** **Infer** where the material in the well came from.

**3.** If each day you add water to the sand around your well, the sand will stay moist. The water you add is like rain. How does rain affect a well?

**4.** **Predict** what will happen to your well if it doesn't "rain" for a few days. Explain your prediction. Then **test** it.

> ### INVESTIGATE FURTHER!
>
> #### EXPERIMENT
> Do this activity again, but this time use clay soil or topsoil instead of sand. Describe the results. Infer which of the materials you used works best with a well.

D21

## Investigate Further

## Experiment

Students will most likely record that clay soil allowed almost no water to pass into the well. Topsoil allowed some water to pass through, but less than sand did. They should infer that sand works best for the well. Students should record their results on *Science Notebook* p. 167.

## 2. Guide the Procedure

- Be sure students push the cup all the way down to the bottom of the pie pan and scoop out the sand in step 2.
- For best results, students should soak the sand, but there should not be excess water on top.

**In what kinds of areas might people depend on wells for their drinking water?** Students may suggest remote areas far from sources of fresh water such as lakes and streams. **What might be some disadvantages of using a well to obtain fresh water?** Suggestions may include that the amount of water is dependent on rainfall and that harmful materials in soil may get washed into the well.

Have students record their observations and answer the questions on *Science Notebook* pp. 166–167.

You may wish to have students use the CD-ROM Writer to organize and display their data.

## 3. Assess Performance

### Process Skills Checklist

- Were students' **inferences** based on their findings? Did they understand that the water in the well is the water that soaked into the sand?
- Were students' **predictions** reasonable? Did they understand that the water level in a well changes depending on how much water soaks through the sand?

### Analyze and Conclude

**1.** Students will see water in their well at the same level as the surface of the sand.

**2.** Students should infer that the water came from the surrounding sand.

**3.** Students may respond that rain keeps the well supplied with water.

**4.** Students may predict that if it doesn't "rain" for a few days there will be little or no water in the well, because rain supplies the water that trickles through the sand.

# Activity Soak It Up!

**Preview** *Students focus on how well different earth materials soak up and hold water and should find that most water passed quickly through the gravel, less quickly through the sand, and still less quickly through the soil.*

**Advance Preparation** *See p. D4b.*

## 1. Get Ready

**Time** about 30 minutes

**Grouping** groups of 3–4

**Multi-Age Strategy** Students who are adept at measuring could aid others in determining and recording the correct measurements.

**Materials Hints** If they are available, you might use plastic funnels in place of the plastic soda bottles.

**Safety** Review safety precautions with students.

## 2. Guide the Procedure

- For best results, each of the earth materials should be dry at the start of the activity.

- As students hold the funnel upside down, a group member should hold the cheesecloth around the bottle neck in case the rubber band doesn't hold.

■ **In step 4, why do you think you need to wait one minute before you take the funnel with gravel out of the bottle?** Most students will say to give the water enough time to flow out of the funnel. **Why will you also have to wait one minute before taking out the funnel with sand and then the one with soil?** So that the length of time will not be a factor that affects the results.

---

# Activity

## Soak It Up!

*Do all kinds of earth materials hold fresh water equally well? In this activity you'll find out.*

- - - - - - - - - - - - - - - - - - - - - - -

### Procedure

**1.** Cover your work area with newspaper. Use the top part of a plastic soda bottle as a funnel. Place a piece of cheesecloth over the opening in the neck of the funnel as shown. Hold the cheesecloth tightly in place with a rubber band.

**2.** Place the funnel, neck down, in the bottom part of the bottle.

**3.** Fill the funnel halfway with gravel.

**4.** Pour 250 mL of water into a measuring cup. Now pour the water into the funnel. Wait one minute.

Step 1

Step 4

D22

---

## 👤 Responding to Individual Needs

**Kinesthetic Activity** Have students feel each earth material as it is placed in the funnel to get an idea of the sizes of the particles. From the particles' sizes, students can infer the sizes of the spaces between the particles. Large particles, such as gravel, will have large spaces between them, while smaller particles will have smaller spaces.

**5.** After one minute, move the funnel to an empty container. Pour the water from the bottom part of the bottle into the empty measuring cup. Measure the amount of water that passed through the gravel.

**6.** Make a chart like the one shown in your *Science Notebook*.

| Earth Material | Water That Passed Through in One Minute (in mL) |
|---|---|
| Gravel | |
| Sand | |
| Soil | |

**7.** Record your measurements in the chart. Empty the measuring cup and the funnel, and rinse off the cheesecloth.

**8.** Talk with your group about your results. Predict what will happen if you repeat the activity, first using sand and then using soil. Record your predictions.

**9.** Repeat steps 2 through 5 and step 7 using sand and then soil. Record all your measurements in your chart.

### Analyze and Conclude

**1.** Through which material did the water pass the fastest? the slowest? Compare your predictions with the results.

**2.** Which material tested in this activity held water the best? How do you know?

**3.** From your observations, infer what can happen to rainwater when it falls on different kinds of ground.

---

**UNIT PROJECT LINK**

Imagine your company has been chosen to design a water system for Waterville, a planned community. What questions will you need to answer before selecting a source of water for the town? Study the brochure on Waterville, then choose a water source for the town.

**D23**

---

As students are stating their predictions, encourage them to give reasons for them also.

Have students record their predictions, observations, and question answers on *Science Notebook* p. 168.

You may wish to have students use the CD-ROM Spreadsheet to draw charts and to display their data.

## 3. Assess Performance

### Process Skills Checklist

- Were students' **measurements** accurate? Was their data reasonable or did some data seem too out-of-place to have resulted from the correct procedure?

- Did students make **predictions**? Were their predictions based on their experience with the first trial using gravel?

- Did students **record** and **interpret their data** correctly? Could they use their data to tell which material held water the best?

### Analyze and Conclude

**1.** Water should pass most rapidly through gravel and most slowly through soil.

**2.** The soil held water best because less water passed through it.

**3.** When rainwater falls, it soaks into and passes through different kinds of ground at different rates. Rainwater passes through sand and gravel more quickly than through soil.

---

## Investigate Further

### Unit Project Link

Tell students that before selecting a water source and designing a water system for Waterville, their company needs to find out what sources of water are available. Use Unit Project Masters D1–D5 (TRB pp. 64–68) to research the answers to the following questions. Are there any lakes or rivers nearby? Is there a sufficient supply of ground water? How much rain falls each year? Is there any water pollution that could affect the source of water chosen for the town? Would a combination of water sources be best? Encourage students to record their answers and ideas on *Science Notebook* p. 169. After students have obtained answers to their questions, they should use this information to choose a water source for Waterville.

# Bring Water Home

**Preview** *Students focus on how people in different parts of the world solve the problem of obtaining fresh water.*

## 1. Get Ready

### Background

- Some parts of the world have serious freshwater problems because the climate has changed in these places, causing a decrease in rainfall. If these places have growing populations, their water supply is no longer sufficient. Too many people and livestock compete for too little water.

- Regions in the world with water shortages include northern Africa, parts of India, northern China, the Middle East, Mexico, and parts of the southwestern United States. Many of these places have the facilities for obtaining water, such as wells, pipes, and faucets, but too many people are using up a small supply of water.

### Discussion Starter

**Where does your drinking water come from?** Students should think beyond the faucet. Many students may be aware of the source of their water, whether it be a well, a river, or a lake. If students get their water from a well, Ask: **Where does the well water come from?** Students should be able to relate to their experience with the activity *Well, Well* to realize that well water comes from water that soaks into the ground.

## 2. Guide the Discussion

*Choose from the following strategies to facilitate discussion.*

### Responding to Individual Needs

**Auditory Activity** Have students work in groups to discuss the solutions that other people in the world have used to overcome water shortages. Each member of the group can summarize a different solution.

# Bring Water Home

 Imagine coming home from school, feeling tired. But before you can rest, you have a chore to do. You have to take a bucket to the town well to bring water home. Most people living in the United States today are lucky—they've never had a reason to do such a chore.

But not all Americans have easy access to water. Every day, people who live in Fox Springs, Alaska, drive to a spring. A spring is a water source where water flows naturally from the ground. People fill containers with the spring water, then drive home. Some people have to drive 16 km (10 mi) every time they need water!

In many villages in Africa, it's easier to get water than it used to be. In the past, people hauled water in buckets or pails from rivers and lakes. Now most villages have wells where people can get fresh water.

▲ Lining up for spring water in Fox Springs, Alaska

▲ Getting water from a well in Mali, in Africa

D24

## Integrating the Curriculum

### Science & Math

**TOTALING**   **What to Do** Help students become aware of how much water some people waste in the simple task of brushing teeth. At home, have each student collect and measure the amount of water wasted if a faucet is allowed to run while brushing one's teeth. **What's the Result?** Let students share their results. Help them calculate how much water was wasted by the class, on average. **How could you find out how much water would be wasted if all of you brushed your teeth twice a day and let the water run?** Multiply the class average by two. **How could people use water more wisely when they are brushing their teeth?** Turn the water on only when it is needed.

▲ **Look for the white pipe coming from the roof of this house in Bermuda.**

On islands such as Bermuda, a rainstorm is a welcome event. The roofs of homes are built in such a way that the rainwater is collected. A pipe funnels the water to tanks under the homes. When it doesn't rain much, the people who rely on such systems must buy water.

▲ **Burmese women filling water jugs from the Irrawaddy**

Tunisia is a country in northern Africa. Parts of Tunisia are in the Sahara, a desert. Some people get their water from wells at an oasis. An oasis is an area in a desert where water is near Earth's surface.

▲ **An oasis in Tunisia, in Africa**

The Irrawaddy is a river that flows through central Burma, a country in Southeast Asia. The Irrawaddy supplies people with drinking water. The river water is also used for growing rice. Rice is a very important part of the diet of people in Burma.

More than 2 billion people on Earth do not have a plentiful, nearby source of fresh water. The next time you turn on a faucet, think about how lucky you are. ∎

**D25**

# Investigate Further

## Cultural Connection

**USING MAPS**

**What to Do** Help students locate on a map the places shown on pp. D24–D25 of the student text. Point out that these places are located in different areas all around the world. These places are the homes of people from several different cultures. Ask: **What might be different about these people?** Language, religious beliefs, jobs, wealth, traditions, and so on **What is the same about these people?** They have the same basic needs that other people have.
**What's the Result?** Discuss the universal need for water. **Why do some people get water one way and other people get water another way?** Students should discuss how different people, and different cultures, obtain water depending on the local conditions and resources.

## Identifying and Solving Problems

**If water didn't flow from the faucets in your area, which of these ways to get water might you try?** Students may opt for taking containers to a safe source and transporting water home. They might also try putting containers on the roof to collect rainwater.

◼ **What problems have to be solved before each of the water collection methods in the text can work?** In Fox Springs, Alaska, people need to have containers to hold water. People need to be careful not to pollute the ground water, since that is their source of water. On Bermuda, people have to install pipes and other equipment on new homes to collect rainwater. In Tunisia, people must find a way to get to the oasis on a regular basis to take water from the wells.

## Connecting to the Activities

• *Well, Well, p. D20*
**In the activity, what if you had pushed the cup only halfway into the sand? Do you think the well would have collected as much water?** No. The well would not have been deep enough to reach the ground water. **Why? If a well runs dry, what might have to be done?** The well might have to be dug deeper to reach the lower water level.

## Making Judgments

◼ **Suppose you lived in a place where you had to walk for half an hour to get water. Is this a chore you would find hard to do?** Students may say they would find the chore hard to do but it would get easier as they got used to it. There may be some days they wouldn't feel like doing this chore but they would probably still do it because of its importance.

• **What might be fun about doing this chore?** Besides obtaining the water, students might discuss the social aspects of visiting and exchanging news with friends and neighbors.

# 3. Assess Understanding

Students can work in groups of three or four to plan how they would obtain water for their town or city in case of an emergency. Have them list a number of ideas and the advantages and disadvantages of each. Have them share ideas with other groups.

# Getting to the Source

**Preview** *Students focus on sources of surface water and ground water and learn where water is stored and accessed.*

## 1. Get Ready

### Science Terms
surface water, reservoir, ground water, aquifers,

### Background

- Southern California and Arizona are both dry regions where large cities have been built. Water from the Colorado River has been diverted by aqueducts to Los Angeles and San Diego. In 1985, when water from the Colorado River was pumped to Phoenix, Arizona, people in San Diego began losing as much as 20 percent of their water. The people in northwest Mexico also experienced water losses because of this diversion. Students should see that water requires wise management and, as a resource, belongs to everyone.

### Discussion Starter

 **What are the names of some lakes and rivers in your state? Which, if any, supplies your drinking water?** If their water comes from a source, such as a visible lake or river, students may be aware of it. If not, tell them they will soon find out about other places where water comes from.

- **Where does the water in lakes and rivers come from?** Students may respond that rainwater, melting snow, or underground springs are the source of water in lakes and rivers.

## 2. Guide the Discussion

*Choose from the following strategies to facilitate discussion.*

### Making Inferences

- Before students read the text, ask: **Where do cities that do not have surface water like lakes and rivers obtain their water?** Students may infer that the water comes from wells or it's piped from a far-away surface water source.

# Getting to the Source

▲ **In Chicago, people use water pumped from Lake Michigan.**

You know that the water cycle brings fresh water to Earth in the form of precipitation. But where does rainwater and melting snow go? Rainwater and melting snow flow downhill and collect in rivers and lakes or soak into the ground. This water is the source of fresh water for cities.

### On the Waterfront

Some cities are lucky enough to have a natural lake or a moving river nearby. A source of water that already exists on the land, such as a lake or a river, is called **surface water.** Cities that use surface water pump the water out of rivers and lakes, clean it, and send it to homes, schools, and businesses through a network of pipes. Chicago, Illinois; Pittsburgh, Pennsylvania; and St. Louis, Missouri, are cities in the United States that use surface water from nearby lakes and rivers.

### Fresh Water From Far Away

Some cities have to go much farther away to find surface-water sources. New York City's water comes from lakes in the Catskill Mountains, more than 160 km (100 mi) away. The water from these lakes is piped to the city through huge tunnels that are as high as a basketball player standing on another player's shoulders!

D26

## Integrating the Curriculum

### Science & Social Studies

**ANALYZING**

**What to Do** Students can determine why rivers are essential to the development of cities. Ask the class to use the map to find the river on which St. Louis is located. (Mississippi River) Ask students to name three other cities that are on this river. (For example, Minneapolis, Davenport, New Orleans) Ask students to list reasons why the cities were built on the Mississippi.

**What's the Result?** Let students name other cities and then find them on the map. Chances are that each city is near a river or large lake. Even cities along the ocean usually have a river nearby. Discuss the advantages of living near a source of fresh water.

### Storing Surface Water

Some regions have built dams across moving rivers or streams. A dam is a barrier that stretches across a river or stream and blocks the water's movement. The place behind the dam where the water collects and is stored is called a **reservoir** (rez'ər vwär). The water collected in reservoirs by dams on the Colorado River is one source from which Los Angeles, California, gets its water. Phoenix, Arizona, also depends on this river for its fresh water.

### Digging Deep

If there is no surface water near-by, people look underground. Water that soaks into the ground and fills the spaces between soil and rocks is called **ground water**. Remember how well earth materials held water

▲ The Glen Canyon Dam holds back surface water, forming Lake Powell.

in the activity on pages D22 and D23. An underground layer of rock where ground water collects is called an **aquifer** (ak'wə fər). Aquifers are important sources of water.

People drill wells into aquifers to obtain water. ▼

well

aquifer

D27

## Investigate Further

### Research

Students could call the local public-works department to find out where the municipal water utility gets its water. The public-works department would also have more information about how water is cleaned and piped to individual homes.

## Connecting to the Activities

- **Well, Well, p. D20**
**What was the source of the water in the well you made in the activity?** The water came from the soaked sand around it.

**You poured water on the sand when you were making your well. How does water reach the ground material around a real well?** Students should respond that rainwater or melting snow soaks the ground, and the water reaches the ground material around the real well.

## Thinking Critically

- **How does a dam built across a river help provide water?** The dam blocks some of the river's water and causes it to collect in a reservoir. The reservoir increases the supply of water for the city.

- **How might a dam affect the wildlife in the river?** There is less water in the river downstream from the dam. Land animals upstream have been flooded out. These environmental changes may cause some of the wildlife to die.

## Responding to Individual Needs

**Students Acquiring English** Have students look at the drawing of an aquifer on p. D27 and describe in English how water soaks into the ground and accumulates above a layer of rock or clay, through which it cannot pass. Then have students explain in English that a well reaches to this layer, and water is pumped from the aquifer.

Have students research fresh water sources using the Lakes, and Rivers Data Packs on the CD-ROM.

## Identifying and Solving Problems

Focusing students' attention on the drawing of the aquifer, ask: **What happens as people pump more and more water out?** The water level goes down. **What would keep the level of water the same?** Rainwater or melting snow would keep the water level about the same, but in many places, people take water out faster than nature can replenish it.

## 3. Assess Understanding

Challenge students working in groups of three or four to name three cities in the U. S. other than those in the text. For each, students should look at a map and infer what that city's source of water might be—surface water or ground water.

# Close
## the Investigation

### Critical Thinking Skills
**Analyzing, Applying, Expressing Ideas**

**1.** Towns and cities can get water from desalination plants, from wells, and from nearby freshwater sources.

**2.** The picture should show a drawing of a well. Water pipes might be shown leading away from the well.

**Challenge** Have students find out where their water comes from and how it is cleaned. If their water comes from a well on their property, it may be cleaned simply by a filter built into the well. Other water sources may involve a process of water purification. Encourage students to draw diagrams showing this process.

 Have students use the CD-ROM Painter and Writer to draw and label their diagrams.

## Following Up

**Baseline Assessment** Return to the list the class made of sources of drinking water. Ask students if they would like to add any sources to make the list more complete. What new information have they learned about where people get their drinking water?

**Reteaching** Have students work in groups to prepare a poster showing where ground water is stored in an aquifer. They may also want to show a well that takes water from the aquifer. Make sure students label the structures on their posters.

 Use *Science Notebook* p. 170.

**Investigation Review ▶**
Use Investigation Review p. 86 in the *Assessment Guide*.

---

To get water out of an aquifer, people often dig a well. A well is a deep, narrow hole that is dug into the ground, down to the level of ground water. You saw in the activity on pages D20 and D21 how a well works. Wells work because water will flow from soaked soil into holes. Sometimes electric pumps or windmills are used to pump water up the well. Miami, Florida; Honolulu, Hawaii; San Antonio, Texas; and Mexico City, Mexico, have dug wells into aquifers to get fresh water.

Some cities don't have surface fresh water or ground-water aquifers nearby. Santa Barbara, California, is one such city. Santa Barbara gets its supply of fresh water by desalinating water from the Pacific Ocean.

Which one of the sources of fresh water you've learned about is the source your city or town uses? See if you can get to the source. ■

▲ **A windmill can be used to pump ground water from an aquifer.**

---

**INVESTIGATION 3**

**1.** Describe three different ways in which towns and cities can get water for their people to use.

**2.** Imagine you are in charge of finding a water supply for your town. You live in an area that gets lots of rain, but there are no surface-water supplies nearby. Describe and draw a picture of what you would do to get water flowing to your town.

D28

---

## Assessment

**Investigation Review**
**Where Are Sources of Fresh Water Found?**

Name _____ Date _____

**1.** Use the words in the box to complete each sentence.

| surface water | ground water | reservoir | aquifer |
| --- | --- | --- | --- |

a. Rivers and lakes supply people with _surface water_.

b. An underground layer of rock where ground water collects is called an _aquifer_.

c. Water that soaks into the ground and fills the spaces between soil and rocks is called _ground water_.

d. A place where water is collected and stored is called a _reservoir_.

**2.** The drawings show a cross section of the ground at three places. At which place, A, B, or C, would you drill a water well? Explain.

_The well should be drilled at A. The soil and rock layer would_ _hold or trap the water better than the other earth materials._

With the addition of another town, people will be consuming water from the reservoir faster than the water can be replaced. The reservoir will run dry in the future.

**Process Skills**
*Predicting*

Two towns get all their fresh water from the same reservoir. Together, the towns use water equal to the rate at which water collects in the reservoir. What will happen if a third town begins to use the reservoir as a water source? Write your prediction on a separate sheet of paper.

---

## Performance

**Town Meeting** Have students role-play members of a town council and citizens of a community. Explain that the town's water wells are running dry and the council has to decide what to do about it. Have students keep a record of their discussions and any decisions they make.

# REFLECT & EVALUATE

# REFLECT & EVALUATE

## WORD POWER

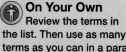

aquifer
condense
evaporate
gas
ground water
liquid
natural resource

precipitation
reservoir
solid
surface water
water cycle
water vapor

 **On Your Own** Review the terms in the list. Then use as many terms as you can in a paragraph about how water changes states.

**With a Partner** Use the terms in the list to make a word-search puzzle. See if your partner can find the hidden terms and tell you what each one means.

### PORTFOLIO

Make a list of all the different ways that you use water. Then find or draw pictures of these ways and use them to make a poster.

## Analyze Information

Study the drawing. Then describe how water moves through the water cycle.

## Assess Performance

Design and carry out an experiment to find out how different sizes of containers affect evaporation. What do the results tell you about evaporation?

## Problem Solving

**1.** Imagine that you're stranded at sea without drinking water. Suddenly a piece of an iceberg floats by. Explain why you should or shouldn't melt the ice for drinking water.

**2.** Imagine it's a cold day and water is boiling on your stove. Then you notice water droplets on the inside of the windows in the kitchen. Explain how the water got there.

**3.** You have a garden in a place where the soil is sandy and tends to dry out quickly. How can you make the soil better for a garden?

**D29**

## Word Power

 **On Your Own** Students' use of the terms should reflect an understanding of their meanings.

 **With a Partner** Word-search puzzles should contain all the terms in the list, spelled correctly.

## Analyze Information

Students should explain that water on Earth's surface is warmed by the Sun and changes to a gas as it evaporates. Then it rises as water vapor to form clouds. Next it cools, condenses back into water droplets, and falls to Earth's surface again as rain.

## Assess Performance

Evaluation could be based on students' ability to design the experiment and to control temperature and amount of water in each container (should be the same) so that the outcome depends only on the size of the containers.

## Problem Solving

**1.** Icebergs are made of fresh water, so you could theoretically melt a piece and drink the water.

**2.** Heat turns the water in the kettle into water vapor. The water vapor moves into the air and when it comes in contact with the cold window it condenses back into liquid water

**3.** You could add material that acts like a sponge and holds the water, such as peat moss.

Use *Science Notebook* pp. 171–172.

### PORTFOLIO

Students might include ways people put water to work, such as drinking, washing, and farming, along with ways they use water for recreation, such as swimming, fishing, and boating. Display the finished posters so students can see each others' work.

## Chapter Test pp. 87 – 88 in the Assessment Guide

# CHAPTER 2 — WONDERS OF WATER

| Subconcepts | Activities | Materials |
|---|---|---|
| **Investigation 1  What Happens to Water in Pipes?** | | |
| Water pressure allows water to flow through pipes; because water expands as it freezes, pipes can break.<br><br>*Suggested Pacing:* 2–3 class periods<br>**Standards**<br> pp. 129, 141<br>**Benchmarks**<br> pp. 68, 264 | **The Pressure's On,** p. D32<br>*Science Processes:* observe; predict; collect, record, and interpret data; make hypotheses; experiment; make and use models<br><br>**Tower Power,** p. D34<br>*Science Processes:* observe; infer; collect, record, and interpret data | masking tape\*, empty milk carton (1-pint) with three holes at different heights, water, large baking pan\*, *Science Notebook* p. 175<br><br>funnel\*, plastic tubing\*, masking tape\*, pin\*, metric ruler\*, baking pan\*, water, *Science Notebook* pp.177–178 |
| **Investigation 2  How Does Drinking Water Vary?** | | |
| The flavor and other properties of drinking water can vary due to the dissolved mineral and chemical content.<br><br>*Suggested Pacing:* 2–3 class periods<br>**Standards**<br> pp. 129, 141<br>**Benchmarks**<br> p. 264 | **Water Taste-Test,** p. D40<br>*Science Processes:* observe, classify, communicate, infer<br><br><br>**Hard and Soft Water,** p. D42<br>*Science Processes:* observe; classify; infer; collect, record, and interpret data; identify and control variables; experiment | marker\*, small paper cups\*, 3 water samples in 3 bottles marked *A*, *B*, and *C*, *Science Notebook* p. 181<br><br>goggles\*, grease pencil\*, 2 small clear plastic vials with lids\*, graduate\*, hard water, dropper\*, liquid dish soap\*, soft water, *Science Notebook* pp. 182–183 |
| **Investigation 3  What Things in Water Can Be Harmful?** | | |
| Materials dissolved or suspended in water may make it unfit to drink.<br><br>*Suggested Pacing:* 2–3 class periods<br>**Standards**<br> pp. 129, 138, 141<br>**Benchmarks**<br> p. 264 | **Let's Clear This Up,** p. D46<br>*Science Processes:* classify, predict, make hypotheses, experiment, make and use models<br><br>**Not As Clear As It Looks,** p. D48<br>*Science Processes:* observe; measure/use numbers; infer; collect, record, and interpret data; identify and control variables | goggles\*, plastic soda bottle cut in half, cheesecloth\*, rubber band\*, fine gravel\*, sand\*, plastic jar with lid\*, spoon\*, soil\*, twigs, leaves, water, *Science Notebook* p. 185<br><br>goggles\*, grease pencil\*, 2 clear plastic cups\*, metric measuring cup\*, aquarium water, tap water, liquid fertilizer\*, dropper\*, clear plastic wrap\*, 2 rubber bands\*, hand lens\*, *Science Notebook* p. 187 |

Step 3

3. Take a small sip of each sample.

4. With your group **rank** the samples 1, 2, 3, using 1 for the water sample you liked best, and so on. Keep sipping until you all agree. **Record** your group's ranking in your *Science Notebook*.

### Analyze and Conclude

1. **Compare** your group's ranking with the rankings of other groups. Did most groups agree with your choices, or did they disagree?

2. **Tally** the results from your class. Which sample got the most first-place votes?

3. What can you **infer** about the source of each water sample? Do you think the samples came from the same source or from different sources? Explain your inferences.

4. Find out from your teacher where each water sample came from. Do the results surprise you? If so, explain why.

D41

## Investigate Further

### Using the Trade Book

WATER PATHS **What to Do** Challenge students to think of some of the things that could affect the taste of water. They could use *DRIP DROP Water's Journey* by Eve and Albert Stwertka to trace the path of water from nature to their homes and back again, identifying any factors that could add or subtract something from the water's taste.

**What's the Result?** Students could make a chart showing the things they think might affect the water's taste and the point in the cycle where they occur.

 Have students use the CD-ROM Spreadsheet to make their charts.

**Materials Hints** Samples should be taken from the water fountain; spring water and distilled water are sold in supermarkets.

**Safety** Review safety precautions with students.

## 2. Guide the Procedure

• Be sure that each student marks and uses his or her own individual set of cups.

• Help the groups compare results by making a chart, with a column for each sample, on the chalkboard. Note each group's rank for Sample A in its column; do the same for the other samples. Students can use this data to compare their rankings to those of other groups.

**Why might the water samples taste different?** Students may mention that different substances can be dissolved in water.

Have students record data and answer questions on *Science Notebook* p. 181.

You may wish to have students use the CD-ROM Spreadsheet to organize and display their group's data.

## 3. Assess Performance

### Process Skills Checklist

• Did students use their sense of taste to **observe** differences in the water samples?

• Were group members able to **communicate** their observations in order to rank the samples?

• Did students **make inferences** about the sources of the water samples?

### Analyze and Conclude

1. Groups' rankings should reflect taste preferences. Encourage students to discuss what they liked or disliked about the samples so they can see that tastes vary.

2. Bottled spring water may be the preference of most students, though the water fountain sample may also be a popular choice.

3. Students should infer that the samples came from different sources because each tasted different. They might also realize that water can contain invisible (to the eye) ingredients that can affect its taste.

4. Students may be surprised to learn that distilled water they consider "pure" doesn't taste very good. They may also be surprised if they preferred water fountain water over an expensive store-bought spring water.

# Activity Hard and Soft Water

**Preview** *Students predict what happens when a drop of detergent is shaken in a sample of "hard" and "soft" water and compare results with predictions.*

**Advance Preparation** *See p. D30b.*

## 1. Get Ready

**Time** 45 minutes

**Grouping** groups of 3–4

 **Collaborative Strategy** One student can prepare the hard water vial; another, the soft water vial. A third can see that both vials are shaken the same number of times.

**Safety** Clean up any spills immediately. Have students wear goggles during this activity.

## 2. Guide the Procedure

- Go over the entire procedure with students before they begin the experiment. They should not shake the vials when they first add the soap.

- Suggest that the students try to shake both vials in the same manner (either vigorously or gently).

Have students draw, record data, and answer questions on *Science Notebook,* pp. 182–183.

You may wish to have students use the CD-ROM Spreadsheet to organize and display their data. The Painter can be used to draw illustrations of the results.

## 3. Assess Performance

### Process Skills Checklist

- Did students **predict** how the hard and soft water would react after shaking?
- Was the shaking monitored to **control variables**?
- Did students **observe and record** changes in the mixtures after they shook the vials?

### Analyze and Conclude

1. Soft water produces more suds than hard water.
2. Soft water makes washing more efficient.
3. Bring water samples in clean containers. Use hard and soft water as controls.

---

# Activity
## Hard and Soft Water

*In this activity you'll find out how hard water and soft water differ.*

### Procedure

**1.** Label a vial *hard water*. Put 10 mL of hard water into it. Add one drop of dish soap. Put the lid on.

**2.** Label a second vial *soft water*. Put 10 mL of soft water into it. Add one drop of dish soap. Put the lid on.

**3.** Predict which vial will have the most suds after being shaken. Record your prediction in your *Science Notebook*.

**4.** Shake both vials back and forth the same number of times. Observe each vial and record your observations.

Step 4

### Analyze and Conclude

**1.** What did you observe about hard water and soft water? How did your prediction compare with the results?

**2.** A water softener can change hard water into soft water. Infer why people sometimes buy water softeners for their homes.

**3.** Repeat this activity with a water sample from home. Do you have hard water or soft water?

D42

---

 ## Responding to Individual Needs

**Visual/Spatial Activity** Reinforce the concepts of this activity by having students make a drawing of the results of the experiment and explain the results in one or more captions. Have students compare their drawings with others'.

 Have students use the CD-ROM Painter and Writer to draw and label their drawings.

# A Matter of Taste

"Why does Grandma's water taste so different from our water?" asked Alisha.

"I don't know," said Mark. "Maybe Grandma flavors her water!"

Of course, Grandma doesn't flavor her water. But does Grandma's water really taste different?

### No Taste

Most people think water has no taste, but it does. If you tasted water samples from many different places, you would find out that water from each region has its own flavor.

The taste of water depends on the chemicals (kem'i kəlz) and minerals (min'ər əlz) found in the water. Chemicals are added to water at treatment plants to kill germs. One chemical, called chlorine (klôr'ēn), not only kills germs but can also add a taste and smell to water. Drinking water that has a lot of chlorine in it may smell and taste like the water in a swimming pool.

D43

---

## Investigate Further

 ### Science, Technology & Society

**WATER SUPPLY** **What to Do** Students can use a community directory to contact the local water utility to find out (1) whether their water supply comes from surface water or underground sources; (2) what chemicals and minerals are added to the water before it is distributed; (3) whether their water supply is naturally "hard" or "soft."

**What's the Result?** Results of the investigation could be submitted to the school or local newspaper as a feature story. Diagrams or photographs could illustrate the story. Emphasize to students that there is a direct correlation between their findings and the taste of their local water.

 Have students use the CD-ROM Painter to create their illustrations.

---

# A Matter of Taste

**Preview** *Students focus on dissolved minerals found in water and how these minerals affect the taste of water.*

## 1. Get Ready

**Science Terms** dissolve, hard water, soft water, distilled water

### Background

- Hydrogen fluoride and other fluorine compounds can help to prevent tooth decay. Many large communities add these compounds to water during the treatment process. Some people think that the addition of fluorine compounds can cause more harm than good. In the past several decades, conflicting information about this issue has prompted some communities to vote to discontinue the practice of adding fluorides to the water. The scientific evidence available today is not strong enough to prove conclusively that fluorides should or should not be added to water.

### Discussion Starter

- **When you visited a relative or friend in another town, how did the water taste in that town?** Prompt students to use descriptive words to explain differences in water. Ask which taste they prefer and why. Find out if they discussed this with the friend or relative they visited.

- **Why does water taste different from place to place?** Encourage students to note that water supplies come from different sources. Water picks up minerals from surrounding soil and rocks; these minerals may differ from region to region, creating different flavors in the water. Towns may also use different processes to purify their water; these additives also affect taste.

# 2. Guide the Discussion

*Choose from the following strategies to facilitate discussion.*

## Making Comparisons

**Will your neighbor's water taste the same as the water in your home, or will it have a different flavor?** In a town, all water usually comes from the town's water system; neighbors' water should taste the same. In rural areas, water may be drawn from wells and taste different from a neighbor's water.

## Connecting to the Activities

- *Water Taste-Test, p. D40*

**You found that people prefer different tastes in the water they drink. Can you think of ways people might change the flavor of the water in their homes?** Water purifiers and filters are available to remove minerals or chemicals from water to change its taste.

- *Hard and Soft Water, p. D42*

**Where can you see evidence of the types of soils and rocks that provide the minerals dissolved in water?** Road cuts often are good places to see exposed bedrock. Creeks and rivers are other good sites to view soil banks and rock outcroppings. Students may have noticed differences between soil and rocks in different geographic areas.

## Responding to Individual Needs

**Visual/Spatial Activity** Have students brainstorm to list words that describe water samples they have tasted. Then provide crayons, colored pencils, or markers so they can draw the words in shapes that relate to water. For example, students might shape each letter to depict a drop of water, or shape a word's letters to form a pitcher. Encourage students to share their efforts with the class.

# 3. Assess Understanding

Pairs of students can draw a web diagram that represents each type of water discussed in the resource. The diagrams should note characteristics for each type of water. Encourage students to share their drawings with the class. Use the Activity Support Master, "Word Web" (TRB p. 46).

▲ Streams dissolve lots of minerals.

### Having a Hard Time

Minerals in water come from the soil and rocks over which water passes. Moving water dissolves (di zälvz′) these minerals. When minerals **dissolve**, they mix with water and separate into very tiny parts that cannot be seen. Have you ever mixed sugar with water? As you stir the mixture, the sugar dissolves and you can no longer see it. Water dissolves minerals in much the same way. Even though we can't see these minerals, we can taste them.

When water contains large amounts of dissolved minerals, that water is called **hard water**. It's difficult to get things clean with hard water. That's because the minerals in hard water keep soap from dissolving easily. Recall that hard water made less suds in the activity on page D42. Other minerals in hard water—iron and copper, for example—produce stains. Hard water can stain clothing, sinks, and tubs.

### Making It Soft

Water containing few minerals is called **soft water**. In some towns, the minerals are removed before the water reaches people's homes. In other towns, households treat their own water to remove the minerals before they use the water.

If water did not have any minerals, chemicals, or air in it, the water would be flat, or tasteless. **Distilled water** is water without any minerals or chemicals in it. It is pure water.

▲ Dissolved minerals in water can leave stains in a sink.

D44

# Integrating the Curriculum

## Science & Math

**GRAPHING**

**What to Do** Ask students to count how many different brands of bottled water they find the next time they visit a grocery store. Each brand should be categorized (spring water, carbonated water, distilled water, and so on). Have students present their combined findings in one large graph.

Have students use the CD-ROM Grapher to graph results.

**What's the Result?** **What type of water has the most brands? Why?** The number of brands may vary by location. If there are many brands of spring water, for example, students might hypothesize that people do not like the taste of the town's tap water. Invite the class to propose a way to test its hypothesis.

▲ Water must be clean, clear, free of odors, and must taste good.

Distilled water is made by evaporating water to separate it from minerals and chemicals. The water vapor is then condensed. Recall how the distilled water tasted in the activity on pages D40 and D41. Water companies hire people to taste water before it's sold to towns and cities. If the water doesn't have a good taste, what do you think the water companies do? They add some more chemicals and minerals to the water!

Water in different regions of the country will have different tastes, depending on the minerals and chemicals in the water. That's why water may have a different taste at Grandma's house than it does at yours. ■

— INVESTIGATION 2 —

1. A cousin visits you from another town. She says your water tastes different from hers. Explain to her why this may be so.

2. Water that has no minerals and chemicals tastes as bad as water that has too many minerals and chemicals. Explain what this means.

D45

 Assessment

## Portfolio

**In My Opinion** Suggest that students write letters to the editor of their local newspaper stating their opinions about water quality. Issues may include the taste of water, the purity of water in local swimming areas, and any water pollution in the area. Encourage students to share their letters with the class before sending them to the newspaper.

**Investigation Review**
**How Does Drinking Water Vary?**

Name _____ Date _____

1. Circle the word that best completes each sentence.
   a. Water that does not make a lot of suds when detergent is added to it is (hard, soft) water.
   b. Some people "treat" (hard, soft) water by running it through a water softener.
   c. If you like to take bubble baths with lots of bubbles, you should use (hard, soft) water.
   d. Most people prefer the taste of water that has (some, no) dissolved minerals in it.

2. The harder the water, the more minerals it has dissolved in it. Read the descriptions of the water samples. Then answer the questions.
   SAMPLE A: Water collected from a mineral spring at Yellowstone National Park
   SAMPLE B: Rainwater
   SAMPLE C: Distilled Water
   a. Which sample would probably contain the most dissolved minerals? ___A___
   b. Which sample(s) would probably contain the least dissolved minerals? __B and C__
   c. Which sample(s) would most likely be labeled "soft" water? __B and C__
   d. Which sample might be labeled "hard water"? ___A___ Students might say they could mix detergent with two water samples. Detergent makes more suds in soft water than in hard water. Students might also propose a "taste test."

**Process Skills**
**Making and Using a Model, Hypothesizing**
How could you demonstrate that hard water and soft water are different? Write your answer on a separate sheet of paper.

# Close
## the Investigation

**Critical Thinking Skills**
**Synthesizing, Generating Ideas, Expressing Ideas**

**1.** Students should explain that minerals and chemicals added to water affect its taste. From one town to another, these chemicals and minerals may be different.

**2.** Water with no minerals or chemicals can taste flat. Water with too many minerals or chemicals can taste unpleasant.

**Challenge** Have students work in pairs or small groups to name beverages that can vary in taste from one brand to another. Responses may include juices, soft drinks, and milk. Encourage groups to share their lists with the class and to think of explanations for the taste differences.

## Following Up

**Baseline Assessment** Return to the class list of different types of drinking water. Add any new responses from students, and then point out how the list has changed. Ask: **What do we now know about the taste of water?** Water's taste can vary depending on the chemicals and minerals dissolved in it.

**Reteaching** Use three different kinds of apples (such as Macintosh, Red Delicious, and Granny Smith) as another way to approach the subject of different tastes. You might have students sample a piece of each apple and discuss differences in taste and texture. Note: Be aware of any food allergies students might have.

Use *Science Notebook* p. 184.

◀ **Investigation Review**
Use Investigation Review p. 90 in the *Assessment Guide.*

# WHAT THINGS IN WATER CAN BE HARMFUL?

## Planner

**Subconcept** Materials dissolved or suspended in water may make it unfit to drink.

**Objectives**
- **Make and use models** of water filtration systems.
- **Observe** the growth of organisms in water.
- **Investigate** the kinds of organisms that live in water and how they can be removed from water.

**Pacing** 2–3 class periods

**Science Term** germ

## Activate Prior Knowledge

**Baseline Assessment** Ask: **Where have you seen dirty or polluted water?** Responses may include puddles and standing water; water that was used for cleaning; and dirty or polluted waterways, such as ponds, creeks, rivers, and lakes. List class responses and save them for Following Up.

# Activity  Let's Clear This Up

**Preview** *Students observe water being filtered.*

**Advance Preparation** *See p. D30b.*

## 1. Get Ready

**Time** about 45 minutes

**Grouping** groups of 3–4

**Materials Hints** Use clear plastic soda bottles to filter water. Supply plenty of sand and gravel.

**Collaborative Strategy** Two students can prepare the filter while other students prepare the water-soil mixture.

**Safety** Wear goggles during this activity.

---

# WHAT THINGS IN WATER CAN BE HARMFUL?

What kinds of harmful things are in fresh water? How can water be made safe for drinking? You'll investigate these questions and find their answers.

# Activity

## Let's Clear This Up

*Freshwater sources have soil, rocks, twigs, and other unwanted items in them. Find out how filtering water is an important step in cleaning water.*

**Procedure**

**1.** Make a model of a water-filtering system. Use the top part of a plastic soda bottle as a funnel. With a group member, use a rubber band to attach a piece of cheesecloth to the end of the funnel.

**2.** Set the funnel in the bottom part of the bottle. Put a layer of fine gravel into the funnel. Then add a layer of sand over the gravel. The materials in the funnel are part of your filtering system.

Step 2

**D46**

**MATERIALS**
- goggles
- plastic soda bottle, cut in half
- cheesecloth
- rubber band
- fine gravel
- sand
- plastic jar with lid
- spoon
- soil, twigs, leaves
- water
- *Science Notebook*

**SAFETY**
Wear goggles during this activity. Do not taste any materials used in this activity.

---

 # Responding to Individual Needs

**Inclusion Activity** It will be easier for challenged students to manipulate a coffee filter in order to clean water. Have students place a paper coffee filter inside a plastic funnel and then slowly pour muddy water into the funnel. Clean water will drip from the spout of the funnel. Have students use a plastic bowl or cup to catch the drips of clean water. Caution students that although the water may look clean, it is not safe to drink as it may contain invisible impurities.

**3.** Pour water into a plastic jar until it is three-fourths full. Add two spoonfuls of soil and a few twigs and leaves to the water. Screw the lid tightly on the jar. Shake up the mixture to make muddy water. This mixture is like the water that may be in a reservoir or river.

**4.** Talk with your group and predict what you will see if you pour the muddy water through the filter. Record your prediction in your *Science Notebook*.

**5.** Slowly pour the jar of muddy water through the filtering system in the funnel. Observe the material that passes through the funnel into the base of the plastic bottle. Record your observations.

### Analyze and Conclude

**1.** Compare your prediction with your results.

**2.** Filtering is one step in making surface water safe for use in homes. Hypothesize how filtering changes muddy water.

**3.** How is what happens to the muddy water in your model of a water-filtering system like what happens to rainwater when it falls on the ground?

#### INVESTIGATE FURTHER!

##### EXPERIMENT

What other materials do you think could be used to filter water? Do this activity again using different materials in your funnel. See how clean you can make the water. **Caution:** Do not drink your filtered water. Share your results with your class.

**D47**

## Investigate Further

### Experiment

Supply materials such as cotton gauze pads, cheesecloth, paper towels, coffee filters, newspaper, and mesh screening. Allow students to label and save samples of water filtered through different materials and to compare the samples to see which materials are the most effective filters. Remind students that they should not drink the water and to clean up any spills immediately. **Which materials worked best to filter water? Why do you think that is?** Students should find that the materials with the finest mesh filter most effectively. These materials allow the fewest particles to pass. Have students record their results on *Science Notebook* p. 186.

## 2. Guide the Procedure

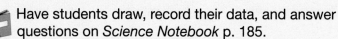

- Make sure students pour the muddy water slowly through the filtering system. Pouring too fast may cause muddy water to overflow the filter, or wash out the sand and gravel.

- Allow students to use as much sand and gravel as they wish.

Have students draw, record their data, and answer questions on *Science Notebook* p. 185.

You may wish to have students use the CD-ROM Writer to record their data.

## 3. Assess Performance

### Process Skills Checklist

- Were students able to **make** and **use a model** of a filtration system? Did they use the model to **observe** how a filter removes impurities?

- Did students draw on past experience to **predict** results?

- Did students use their observations to **hypothesize** how filters work?

### Analyze and Conclude

**1.** Students should compare their predictions to their observations.

**2.** Students should hypothesize that the materials in the filter prevent some of the impurities from passing through them.

**3.** Soil and rocks are filtering materials for the rainwater, just as sand, gravel, and cheesecloth are the filtering materials in the model.

# Activity — Not As Clear As It Looks

**Preview** *Students place liquid fertilizer in tap water and aquarium water to observe changes.*

## 1. Get Ready

**Time** 30–45 minutes the first day; 30–45 minutes two days later

**Grouping** groups of 3–4

**Safety** Clean up any spills immediately. Be sure that students wear goggles. Fertilizers can be toxic; caution students about handling the fertilizer and remind them to wash their hands after they handle the cups.

## 2. Guide the Procedure

- Invite students to examine their samples with the hand lens just after they add the fertilizer. You might have them sketch what they see.
- Do not open cups once they are covered with plastic.
- If students cannot observe much change in the aquarium water after two days, allow the samples to stand for another day or so.

 Students may record their data and answer questions on *Science Notebook* p. 187.

 You may wish to have students use the CD-ROM Spreadsheet to organize and display their data in a chart. The Painter could be used to draw what they see when they use the hand lens.

## 3. Assess Performance

### Process Skills Checklist
- Were students able to **measure** the water samples and fertilizer carefully?
- Could students **observe** how the samples changed after two days? Did they **infer** the cause of the changes?
- Were charts and drawings used to **record data** accurately?

### Analyze and Conclude
1. Students should notice that the aquarium water is cloudy and that the tap water is clearer.
2. Living organisms present in aquarium water multiply when fertilizer is added. Tap water has been treated in order to remove these organisms.

---

# Activity

## Not As Clear As It Looks

*Water may contain many living things. In this activity, you'll see why clear water may not be clean water.*

### Procedure

**1.** Use a grease pencil to label a clear plastic cup *Tap Water*. Pour 50 mL of tap water into the cup. Label a second cup *Aquarium Water*. Pour 50 mL of aquarium water into this cup.

**2.** Fertilizer is food for living things. Talk with your group and predict what will happen to the water if you put fertilizer into each cup. Record your prediction in your *Science Notebook*.

**3.** Use a dropper to place 20 drops of liquid fertilizer into each cup, cover with clear plastic wrap, and secure with a rubber band. Place the cups in a window.

**4.** After two days, observe the water in each cup with a hand lens. Record your observations.

Step 3

### Analyze and Conclude

**1.** What did you observe in each cup? How did your prediction compare with your results?

**2.** Changes to the water occurred because of the presence of tiny living things. Infer why they might be present in one cup but not the other.

**D48**

---

## Responding to Individual Needs

**Students Acquiring English** Invite students to describe what they observed in the aquarium water after liquid fertilizer was added, and to write two or three sentences that detail their observations. Pair students and have them read their sentences to each other.

 Have students use the CD-ROM Writer for their observations.

# Wee Beasties!

 They're everywhere and they're multiplying! What are they? They're germs! But what are germs? People use the word **germ** when they're talking about tiny living things that can make them sick.

**These protists are shown about 100 times larger than they actually are.** ▼

### Germs Everywhere

There are different kinds of germs. One group of germs includes protists (prōt′ists). Protists are neither animals nor plants, but they are alive. Many kinds of protists live in water and wet soil.

Another group of germs includes bacteria (bak tir′ē ə). Bacteria are neither animals nor plants. Bacteria live in soil, air, and water.

Protists are so small that they can't be seen with just the eyes. But bacteria are even smaller. About 500 bacteria could fit inside one protist! Fifty million bacteria could live in a single drop of pond water!

### Anton's Discovery

If germs are too small to see, how have people learned about them? To find the answer, you need to know what happened more than 300 years ago. That is when "wee beasties" were discovered.

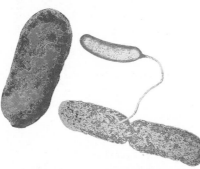

▲ **These bacteria are shown about 10,000 times larger than they actually are.**

D49

## Investigate Further

### Integrating the Sciences

LIFE SCIENCE

**What to Do** Students list everyday events they do or observe at home, in school, or in their community that include cleaning or disinfecting. Examples include washing hands, dishes, pets, and cars; watching a street-cleaning machine; or observing a window washer. Have students organize their observations into categories according to functions: disinfecting, removing dirt, or making things neat. Invite students to illustrate their lists and then to work in groups to explain why they classified actions as they did.

**What's the Result?** Students will realize that actions we call cleaning serve different purposes, but that most of them remove potential contaminants from our environments.

# Wee Beasties!

**Preview** *Students focus on tiny living things in air, water, and soil; they follow the steps in the process of treating water to remove these and other contaminants.*

## 1. Get Ready

**Science Term** germ

### Background

- Not all of the tiny organisms found in water, air, and soil are harmful. Some small organisms, such as algae, serve many useful purposes. Algae are the chief food source for fish and other creatures that live in the water. In Japan, algae are cultivated and harvested for human food. Algae also produce a large amount of the oxygen available on earth.

- Although most algae are found in water or other moist places, algae can also be found on leaves, wood, stones, and tree trunks. A few of the 25,000 species of algae can tolerate high temperatures and live in hot springs, like the ones in Yellowstone Park. Some algae also live in the snow and ice of the Arctic and Antarctic.

### Discussion Starter

**Why should people make certain that they drink pure, clean water?** Encourage speculation about the connection between dirty water and illness. Students probably realize that visible dirt in water can make them sick; they may not realize that tiny germs, invisible to the unaided eye, are in the water and may cause many illnesses.

**What actions can people take to be sure that they have pure, clean water?** Water treatment plants are common in many areas of the country. Some people further insure the purity of their drinking water by using devices called water purifiers.

# 2. Guide the Discussion

*Choose from the following strategies to facilitate discussion.*

## Connecting to the Activities

- ### *Let's Clear This Up*, p. D46
   **Where are water treatment plants located? What is the source of the water treated there?** Water treatment plants are often located near lakes or rivers. They draw water from these sources and treat it for use by towns. Waste treatment plants are also located near bodies of water. They receive water (runoff from streets and waste water from homes and factories) through large pipes, treat it, and return it to rivers or streams.

- ### *Not As Clear As It Looks*, p. D48
  **What do you think you would see if you examined your aquarium water sample under a microscope?** A hand lens magnifies things slightly so that students can see small specks in the water. A microscope would allow them to see details of the tiny organisms called algae. There are many different kinds of algae and their appearance varies.

## Responding to Individual Needs

**Kinesthetic Activity** Provide photographs or drawings of aquatic micro-organisms that can be seen under a microscope. Invite students to make small clay models of the creatures.

To help students visualize the water treatment process, use **Transparency 21,** "Water Treatment Plant."

## Making Comparisons

**Name some places where you think harmful bacteria live. Name some places where harmful bacteria are less likely to live.** Dirty dishes, left-over food, and dirty water are likely sites for hosting harmful bacteria. Places where fewer harmful bacteria exist include swimming pools treated with chlorine, freshly washed hands, and clean dinnerware.

---

In the second half of the 1600s, a young man named Anton van Leeuwenhoek lived in Holland. Anton was interested in improving microscopes (mī′krə skōps). A microscope is a device that has lenses that make very small things look bigger than they really are. Anton looked at many things through his microscopes.

One day, Anton looked at a drop of lake water through a microscope. He saw many tiny things moving around in the water. He called them "wee beasties" because they looked like little animals to him.

### What a Treat

Today we know that the tiny living things Anton saw were *not* animals.

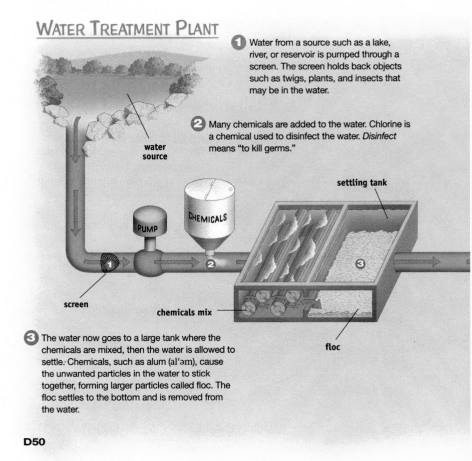

## WATER TREATMENT PLANT

1. Water from a source such as a lake, river, or reservoir is pumped through a screen. The screen holds back objects such as twigs, plants, and insects that may be in the water.

2. Many chemicals are added to the water. Chlorine is a chemical used to disinfect the water. *Disinfect* means "to kill germs."

3. The water now goes to a large tank where the chemicals are mixed, then the water is allowed to settle. Chemicals, such as alum (al′əm), cause the unwanted particles in the water to stick together, forming larger particles called floc. The floc settles to the bottom and is removed from the water.

water source

PUMP

CHEMICALS

settling tank

screen

chemicals mix

floc

**D50**

---

# Investigate Further

## Integrating the Sciences

LIFE SCIENCE

**What to Do** Let students take turns using a microscope to view different kinds of water, such as pond water, water from a puddle, aquarium water, rainwater, and distilled water. Encourage students to draw what they observe.

**What's the Result?**  **Which kind of water had the most living things in it? Why do you think that is?** The water with the most food available for living things will likely have the most organisms.

**Multi-Age Classroom** Encourage students to work in pairs or small groups, with some students preparing the samples and others drawing the results of their observations.

Have students use the CD-ROM Painter for their drawings.

We know they were protists. We also know that protists and bacteria that live in fresh water can be harmful to people by causing illness.

Other unwanted living things in fresh water include algae (al'jē). Think back to the activity you did on page D48. After you added fertilizer to water, tiny living things grew and multiplied. These living things were algae.

To make fresh water safe for people to use, the water must first be filtered. After filtering, the water must be treated to kill unwanted, harmful living things. These things are done in a water treatment plant. Follow the steps in the process of water being filtered and disinfected (dis in fek'tid) at a water treatment plant in the drawing below.

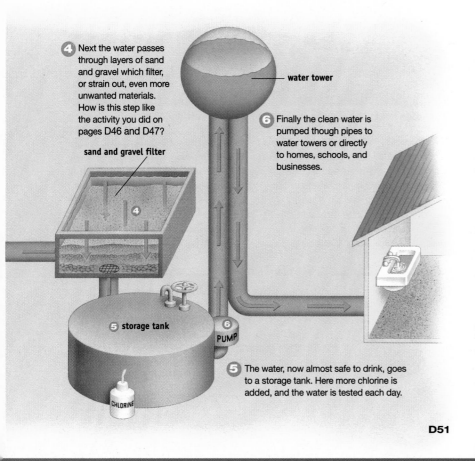

**4** Next the water passes through layers of sand and gravel which filter, or strain out, even more unwanted materials. How is this step like the activity you did on pages D46 and D47?

**sand and gravel filter**

water tower

**6** Finally the clean water is pumped though pipes to water towers or directly to homes, schools, and businesses.

**5** storage tank

**PUMP**

CHLORINE

**5** The water, now almost safe to drink, goes to a storage tank. Here more chlorine is added, and the water is tested each day.

D51

## Cultural Connection

**What to Do** Share with students that in some villages in Uganda, Africa, people used to walk great distances to get water. Women would fill large jars with water at a well, then walk home balancing one jar on their head and carrying another. Now most of these villages have their own wells. To get some idea of the skill involved, encourage students to try walking across the room, balancing a book on their heads.

**What's the Result?** Ask students to describe how easy or difficult it was to balance the book. Ask: **What additional problems might there be trying to carry a jug of water?** Students may say that the water would slosh around in the jug, making it difficult to keep it balanced.

CARRYING WATER

## Thinking About the Data

**Why don't people add chemicals to lakes and rivers instead of treating water in treatment plants?** Even organisms that are harmful to people are useful in nature. Some bacteria break down waste products, others are food for fish or animals. Chemicals that we add to water might also kill plants, fish, insects, and other animals.

## Responding to Individual Needs

**Gifted and Talented Activity** Challenge students to investigate the environmental issue of acid rain. They could use reference books and periodicals to learn about the causes and effects of acid rain. Provide an opportunity for them to share the information with the class. Students could demonstrate the effects of acid rain by repeating the activity Not As Clear As It Looks. Use pond or aquarium water in both cups, but add a few drops of white vinegar to one cup to increase acidity.

## 3. Assess Understanding

Have pairs of students write a brief description of the water purification process. Encourage them to draw diagrams to accompany their descriptions.

Have students use the CD-ROM Painter and Writer to draw and label their diagrams.

# Close the Investigation

## Critical Thinking Skills
**Synthesizing, Applying**

**1.** You should not drink the water; it may contain harmful bacteria that are too small to see.

**2.** Germs are killed by adding chemicals to the water.

**Challenge** Encourage students to think about water's journey from the treatment plant to their faucets. The water is safe to drink when it leaves the plant.

■ **What can affect the water between the treatment plant and your home?** Water can pick up contaminants if pipes break, or if materials from the pipes themselves (such as lead) leach into the water. Local governments routinely test water in homes and buildings to be sure that the water is safe to drink. If problems are found, residents are alerted to use bottled water or to follow procedures that will make the water safe to drink.

## Following Up

**Baseline Assessment** Return to the list of dirty water sources that the class generated. Add any new suggestions from students. Ask students to suggest ways that water from these sources may be cleaned.

**Reteaching** Draw a diagram of a simple water filter on the chalkboard. Prompt students to explain how it works, and then ask them if filtration is enough to ensure clean drinking water. Discuss why chemicals are needed to be sure that water is safe to drink.

 Use *Science Notebook* p. 188.

**Investigation Review ▶**
Use Investigation Review p. 91 in the *Assessment Guide.*

▲ Sewage treatment plant in the city of Palo Alto, California

### Waste Not, Want Not

Clean water is used to wash people, clothes, dishes, and to flush toilets. It is used to make things in factories. After it is used, the water is no longer clean. The dirty water is called waste water, or sewage (soo'ij). Waste water can't be put back directly into lakes and streams. It must first be cleaned.

Waste water is cleaned in much the same way as drinking water is cleaned. Cleaned waste water can be returned to lakes and rivers, where it becomes part of the water cycle again. ■

—————— **INVESTIGATION 3** ——————

**1.** Imagine that you are hiking in the woods. You are very thirsty, and the water in a nearby pond looks very clean. Would you drink it? Why or why not?

**2.** How are germs in the water killed before the water reaches your home?

**D52**

## Assessment

**Investigation Review**
**What Things in Water Can Be Harmful?**

Name _____ Date _____

**1.** Use the words in the box to complete the sentences.

| boiling | filtering | chemicals |
| germs | soil |

Water from Earth's surface can contain leaves, insects, and __soil__, which makes the water look muddy. These items can be removed by __filtering__. In addition, water can contain tiny living things, called __germs__, that can make people sick. They can be removed by __boiling__. They may also be killed by treating water with __chemicals__.

**2.** The statements below tell how a water treatment plant cleans water. These statements, however, are not in the right order. Put the statements in the correct order.

__2__ Chlorine is added to disinfect the water.

__4__ The water is passed through a sand and gravel filter.

__1__ Water from a source is pumped through a screen.

__3__ Water goes to a settling tank where alum is added and forms floc.

**Process Skills** Mary drank lake water without boiling it.
**Inferring** There may have been harmful bacteria, protists, or algae in it.
Mary and Sally are camping in the wilderness. They both eat and drink the same things. Mary, however, drinks some water directly from a nearby lake, while Sally boils the water to make tea. Why might Mary become ill? Write your answer on a separate sheet of paper. Because Sally boiled her water, these living things were killed.

### Performance

**Newscast** Students work in small groups to prepare a newscast alerting residents that a town's water may be unsafe to drink. Remind students to use as many facts as possible to explain the situation and to cite measures that will be taken in order to correct the problem.

# REFLECT & EVALUATE

## WORD POWER

dissolve
distilled water
germ
gravity
hard water
soft water
water pressure

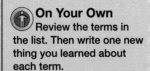 **On Your Own** Review the terms in the list. Then write one new thing you learned about each term.

 **With a Partner** Write each term in the list on one side of an index card and the definition on the other side. Use the cards to quiz your partner.

**PORTFOLIO**

Make a drawing to show how water moves through pipes to get to your bathroom sink. Show all the valves. Is there a main valve that can stop all the water coming into your home? Show it, too.

## Analyze Information

Study the drawing. Two cracks have formed in the water tower. Compare how water will flow out of crack X and crack Y. Explain why the water might flow differently from each crack.

## Assess Performance

Design an experiment to find out if the width of a water pipe can change the pressure of the water coming out of the pipe. After your teacher has reviewed your plan, carry out your experiment. Compare your results with those of others.

## Problem Solving

**1.** Imagine you turned on your water faucet and only drips came out. List all the things that could be causing the problem. What could you do to solve the problem?

**2.** You are a water quality engineer at a water treatment plant. One day the water has an unpleasant taste. Explain what could have happened and what you would do.

**3.** Sometimes during a flood, people are advised to boil water before they drink it. Why does boiling the water makes it safer to drink?

**D53**

---

# REFLECT & EVALUATE

## Word Power

 **On Your Own** Students should describe a scientific bit of information related to each term.

**With a Partner** Students' definitions should be in their own words, but accurate.

## Analyze Information

Water will flow out of crack X slowly but water will spurt out of crack Y with great force. There is more water above crack Y which causes greater water pressure.

## Assess Performance

Evaluation could be based on students' ability to set up two conditions that differ only in the width of the pipes.

## Problem Solving

**1.** Appliances, such as a washing machine, may be turned on or too many people could be using water at the same time. To get more water pressure, you can turn off appliances for a while or just wait until the water pressure returns. There may also be a burst water main under the street. The water company will tell you if this happens.

**2.** Too many or not enough chemicals may have been added to the water. If not enough chemicals are in the water, more can be added. If too many chemicals have been added, then water without chemicals can be added to the water to dilute it.

**3.** Boiling would kill tiny living things in the water that might be harmful to humans.

Use *Science Notebook* pp. 189–190.

**PORTFOLIO**

Encourage students to work with family members to construct their diagrams. The main shut-off valve in an apartment building might be in the basement or a similar area.

---

## Chapter Test pp. 92–93 in the Assessment Guide

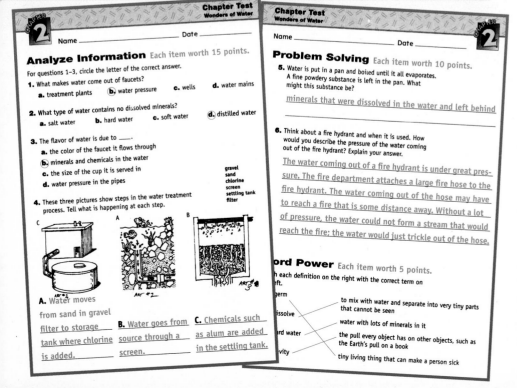

Chapter Test
Wonders of Water

Name _____ Date _____

**Analyze Information** Each item worth 15 points.
For questions 1–3, circle the letter of the correct answer.
**1.** What makes water come out of faucets?
a. treatment plants  **b.** water pressure  c. wells  d. water mains

**2.** What type of water contains no dissolved minerals?
a. salt water  b. hard water  c. soft water  **d.** distilled water

**3.** The flavor of water is due to ___.
a. the color of the faucet it flows through
**b.** minerals and chemicals in the water
c. the size of the cup it is served in
d. water pressure in the pipes

**4.** These three pictures show steps in the water treatment process. Tell what is happening at each step.

A. Water moves from sand in gravel filter to storage tank where chlorine is added.
B. Water goes from source through a screen.
C. Chemicals such as alum are added in the settling tank.

Chapter Test
Wonders of Water

Name _____ Date _____

**Problem Solving** Each item worth 10 points.
**5.** Water is put in a pan and boiled until it all evaporates. A fine powdery substance is left in the pan. What might this substance be?
minerals that were dissolved in the water and left behind

**6.** Think about a fire hydrant and when it is used. How would you describe the pressure of the water coming out of the fire hydrant? Explain your answer.
The water coming out of a fire hydrant is under great pressure. The fire department attaches a large fire hose to the fire hydrant. The water coming out of the hose may have to reach a fire that is some distance away. Without a lot of pressure, the water could not form a stream that would reach the fire; the water would just trickle out of the hose.

gravel
sand
chlorine
screen
settling tank
filter

**Word Power** Each item worth 5 points.
Match each definition on the right with the correct term on the left.
germ
dissolve
hard water
gravity

to mix with water and separate into very tiny parts that cannot be seen
water with lots of minerals in it
the pull every object has on other objects, such as the Earth's pull on a book
tiny living thing that can make a person sick

# CARING FOR OUR WATER

| Subconcepts | Activities | Materials |
|---|---|---|
| **Investigation 1  What Can Happen to Clean Water?** | | |
| Water pollution—caused by agricultural run off, industries, and home septic systems—can be reduced.<br><br>*Suggested Pacing:*  2–3 class periods<br>**Standards**<br>    pp. 129, 140, 141<br>**Benchmarks**<br>    p. 264 | **Not-So-Gentle Rain,** p. D56<br>*Science Processes:*  observe, identify and control variables, make hypotheses | goggles\*, 2 paper cups\*, grease pencil\*, pencil, soil\*, 20 radish seeds\*, metric ruler\*, dropper\*, water, dropper bottle with vinegar\*, *Science Notebook* p. 193 |
| **Investigation 2  How Does Water Pollution Move From Place to Place?** | | |
| Water pollution that reaches, or is released into, the ocean is dispersed by tides and currents.<br><br>*Suggested Pacing:*  2–3 class periods<br>**Standards**<br>    pp. 129, 141<br>**Benchmarks**<br>    p. 264 | **All Washed Up,** p. D64<br>*Science Processes:*  infer, make and use models<br><br>**Going My Way?,** p. D66<br>*Science Processes:*  observe, infer, predict, experiment | goggles\*, rocks, gravel or sand\*, large baking pan\*, water, metric ruler\*, soil\*, spoon\*, cooking oil\*, *Science Notebook* pp. 196–197<br><br>goggles\*, cold tap water, clear plastic aquarium\*, dropper\*, food coloring\*, small jar with lid\*, hot tap water, *Science Notebook* pp. 198–199 |
| **Investigation 3  How Can We Save and Protect Water?** | | |
| Water must be conserved—and pollution cleaned up and prevented—in order to insure that there is enough safe fresh water for everyone's basic needs.<br><br>*Suggested Pacing:*  2–3 class periods<br>**Standards**<br>    pp. 129, 140, 141<br>**Benchmarks**<br>    p. 264 | **Down the Drain,** p. D72<br>*Science Processes:*  measure/use numbers; communicate; infer; collect, record, and interpret data<br><br>**Drops Count,** p. D73<br>*Science Processes:*  measure/use numbers; infer; collect, record, and interpret data | *Science Notebook* p. 202<br><br><br>small empty milk carton, water, graduate\*, cup\*, timer\*, *Science Notebook* p. 203 |

# Overview

In this chapter students investigate the relationship between water quality and the actions of people, discover how water pollution is dispersed, and learn how they can take an active part in conserving and protecting water.

# Chapter Concept

The availability of Earth's water supplies may not keep up with demands; water can be polluted, yet it also can be conserved and pollution can be reduced.

| Advance Preparation | Curriculum Connection | Assessment |
|---|---|---|
| **Not So Gentle Rain**<br>None | Integrating the Sciences TG pp. D58, D59<br>Language Arts TG p. D60<br>Science, Technology & Society TG p. D61<br>The Arts TG p. D62 | **Chapter 3 Baseline Assesssment:**<br>*Science Notebook* pp. 191–192<br><br>**Investigation 1 Baseline Assessment:**<br>TG p. D56<br>**Investigation 1 Review:** AG p. 94<br>**Think It/Write It,** p. D63; *Science Notebook* p. 195<br>**Following Up on Baseline Assessment:**<br>TG p. D63<br>**Portfolio:** TG p. D63 |
| **All Washed Up**<br>None<br><br>**Going My Way?**<br>None | The Arts TG p. D67<br>Cultural Connection TG p. D68<br>Social Studies TG p. D70 | **Investigation 2 Baseline Assessment:**<br>TG p. D64<br>**Investigation 2 Review:** AG p. 95<br>**Think It/Write It,** p. D 71; *Science Notebook* p. 201<br>**Following Up on Baseline Assessment:**<br>TG p. D71<br>**Portfolio:** TG p. D71 |
| **Down the Drain**<br>None<br><br>**Drops Count**<br>Collect 1 pint or 1/2 pint milk cartons from the school cafeteria. Rinse thoroughly. | Science, Technology & Society TG pp. D74, D77<br>Cultural Connection TG p. D75<br>Integrating the Sciences TG p. D76 | **Investigation 3 Baseline Assessment:**<br>TG p. D72<br>**Investigation 3 Review:** AG p. 96<br>**Think It/Write It,** p. D78; *Science Notebook* p. 204<br>**Following Up on Baseline Assessment:**<br>TG p. D78<br>**Performance:** TG p. D78<br><br>**Chapter 3 Summative Assessment**<br>Reflect and Evaluate, p. D79<br>Chapter 3 Review/Test: AG pp. 97–98<br>*Science Notebook* pp. 205–206 |

TG= Teaching Guide   TRB= Teacher Resource Book   AG= Assessment Guide   *Materials in Equipment Kit

## Introducing the Chapter

# Chapter Overview

**Chapter Concept** The availability of Earth's water supplies may not keep up with demands; water can be polluted, yet it also can be conserved and pollution can be reduced.

## Theme: Systems

Water on Earth is part of a system called the water cycle. When pollution moves into the system, it can interact adversely with the living things, soil, and water supplies.

## Common Misconceptions

Students might think that air pollution and water pollution are separate problems and that they need not worry about industrial pollution unless they live near factories.

## Options for
# Setting the Stage

## Warm-Up Activity

 Encourage students to imagine they are scientists investigating the quality of water in a river or lake. Ask them what clues they might look for to determine whether the water is polluted.

Use *Science Notebook* pp. 191–192.

## Discussion Starter:
**Saving Lake Victoria**

Use the photo and text to start a discussion about water pollution.

- **What might cause water pollution in your area?** Industrial waste, pesticides, agricultural runoff, litter on beaches, ocean dumping, oil spills, fuel from pleasure boats

- **What might be done to reduce water pollution?** Advertising, legislation, and various cleanup plans

- **Career:** Environmental Scientist
Environmental scientists study the effects of pollution on the environment. They develop investigation plans using mathematical and scientific concepts. They analyze air, water, and soil samples. Once they find what is causing the pollution, they can devise plans to reduce and counter it.

# CARING FOR OUR WATER

"When the well's dry, we know the worth of water."
—Benjamin Franklin
Franklin said that more than 200 years ago.
Today, the need for clean water is greater than ever.
In this chapter you'll find out why it's important to protect fresh water all over the world.

## Saving Lake Victoria

**P**eter Ochumba is a scientist who studies East Africa's Lake Victoria. He takes water samples and gathers information about the living things in the lake. He also keeps track of activities near the lake that might affect the water.

Ochumba has found that fertilizers, pesticides, and wastes from factories have changed the lake. It has become murky and some fish have died.

Think about Lake Victoria as you explore the investigations in this chapter. Look for changes that might be made to bring the lake back to life.

D54

# Home-School Connection

The Explore at Home activity "Picture This" encourages students to think about sources of pollution. Distribute the activity (TRB p. 18) when students have completed the chapter. Discuss what would happen to a glass of water left uncovered by an open window.

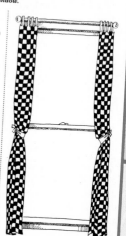

Name _____  Date _____

### PICTURE THIS

*In our science class, we are studying how Earth's water becomes polluted. Think of your window as a picture frame. You and a family member can learn more about pollution by taking a good look at the environment right outside your window.*

**Procedure**

Choose a window in your home. With a family member, look out the window for anything that might be a source of water pollution. Don't forget things that could cause acid rain or chemical pollution. For example, does a neighbor fertilize the lawn or spray pesticides? Are toxic materials being dumped down the drain? Is there an industry nearby that uses water? In the window or on another piece of paper, draw the scene you see. To this scene, add everything that might cause water to become polluted.

**Results**

Would different windows in your home show different sources of pollutants? How do you think a drawing from another part of the country would be different from yours? Talk about ways your family could help conserve water and keep water clean.

◄ Peter Ochumba, African scientist

D55

## Technology Alert

### CD-ROM

**Using Water** and **Nice Save** Enhances or replaces Investigation 3

In **Using Water** students look at an animated cross-section of an apartment. Using a Water Meter probe, students measure the average amount of water used daily by a family of four for water-using activities. Next, students predict who uses the most water: homes, factories, businesses, or public facilities. They view a graph to check their predictions.

In **Nice Save** students predict how much water can be saved each day if water-saving ideas and devices are used. Then they use a Water Meter probe to check their predictions and calculate how much water can be saved each week, month, or year. They finish by watching a video about waste-water treatment.

## Chapter Road Map

**What Can Happen to Clean Water?**

| Activities | Resources |
|---|---|
| ✱ Not-So-Gentle Rain | ✱ Water Worries |
| | Industrial-Revolution Pollution |

**How Does Water Pollution Move From Place to Place?**

| Activities | Resources |
|---|---|
| ✱ All Washed Up | ✱ The Current Idea |
| Going My Way? | Mother of Waters |

**How Can We Save and Protect Water?**

| Activities | Resources |
|---|---|
| ✱ Down the Drain | Isn't Water Free? |
| Drops Count | ✱ A Bargain at Any Price |

### *Pressed for Time?

As you work through the upcoming investigations, focus on the activities and resources identified by the clock.

Look for this symbol in front of questions that help develop Scientific Reasoning Skills.

# WHAT CAN HAPPEN TO CLEAN WATER?

## Planner

**Subconcept** Water pollution — caused by agricultural runoff, industries, and home septic systems — can be reduced.

### Objectives

- **Observe** the effects of acid rain on living things.
- **Identify** common pollutants.
- **Explain** how pollution can be reduced.

**Pacing** 2–3 class periods

**Science Terms** acid rain, polluted

## Activate Prior Knowledge

**Baseline Assessment** Create some "polluted" water by adding ash, soil, oil, detergent, and vinegar to tap water. Give students a sample of polluted water and of clean water. Ask: **How is the polluted water different from the clean water? How did it get that way?** Record students' responses and save them for use in Following Up.

## Activity    Not-So-Gentle Rain

**Preview** *Students focus on how acid rain affects living things and compare the effects of acid water and tap water on radish seeds. Students should find that the radish seeds grown in tap water grew better than those seeds grown in acid water.*

## 1. Get Ready

**Time** about 30 minutes to set up the initial experiment, then about 5 minutes a day for observation during the following two weeks

**Grouping** groups of 3–4

---

# WHAT CAN HAPPEN TO CLEAN WATER?

Suppose you are very thirsty. You go to the water fountain and see a sign that says "Water Is Unsafe. Do Not Drink!" What can happen to clean water to make it unsafe to drink? In this investigation, you'll find out.

## Activity

### Not-So-Gentle Rain

*When fuels are burned, substances can go into the air and change clean rainwater to acid rain. Find out how acid rain affects living things.*

**MATERIALS**
- goggles
- 2 paper cups
- grease pencil
- pencil
- potting soil
- 20 radish seeds
- metric ruler
- dropper
- water
- dropper bottle with vinegar
- *Science Notebook*

**SAFETY**
Wear goggles during this activity. Clean up any spills immediately. Wash your hands when you have finished handling soil.

### Procedure

**1.** Label one paper cup *Tap Water* and another paper cup *Acid Rain*. Use a pencil point to poke a hole in the bottom of each cup.

**2.** Add soil to both cups until they are three-fourths full. Drop 10 radish seeds onto the soil in each cup. Lightly cover the seeds with 1 cm of soil.

Step 2

**D56**

---

## Responding to Individual Needs

**Students Acquiring English** Students can draw their observations over the course of the two weeks. Then they can have a student more proficient in English help them label their drawings in English. Display the drawings in the classroom. Encourage students to pronounce the terms in both languages.

Have students use the CD-ROM Painter and Writer to draw and label their drawings.

**3.** Use a dropper to add plain tap water to the seeds in the cup labeled *Tap Water* to dampen the soil. Add the same number of drops of vinegar, an acid, to the seeds in the cup labeled *Acid Rain*.

Step 3

**4.** With your group, **predict** what will happen to the seeds in each cup. Explain why. **Record** your prediction in your *Science Notebook*.

**5.** Moisten your seeds whenever the soil feels dry. *Use the correct kind of liquid for each cup*.

**6.** **Observe** your seeds every day for two weeks. **Record** your observations. After two weeks, **compare** your observations to your predictions.

### Analyze and Conclude

**1.** Did the seeds sprout in each cup? If so, in which cup did the seedlings grow best? **Hypothesize** what caused the differences.

**2.** **Hypothesize** how acid rain might affect the plants on which it falls.

> **INVESTIGATE FURTHER!**
>
> **RESEARCH**
>
> Find out how much acid rain plants can be watered with and still grow. Set up another experiment, using week-old plants. Share your results with your classmates.

D57

---

## Investigate Further

### Experiment

Let students decide how many drops of vinegar, up to 20, to use to make their acid water. Students should find that with a high enough concentration of vinegar in the water, the plants will eventually die. Students should record their data in their *Science Notebooks* on p. 194.

**Multi-Age Classroom** Ask: **Do all plants react the same way to acid in the soil?** Have groups of students call up or visit a local nursery to find out which plants grow best in a more acidic environment, and which plants will die if there is any acid in the soil. **If the soil has too much acid to grow a particular plant, what can you do about it?** Lime is commonly applied to grass lawns to neutralize the acid in the soil. Encourage students to ask their parents if they have ever applied lime to a lawn.

---

**Multi-Age Strategy** Students who are adept at measuring can help others with the various measurements required in this activity.

**Materials Hints** Vinegar is an acid. Caution students to handle it carefully.

**Safety** Make sure that students wear goggles during this activity. Clean up any spills immediately to prevent accidents. Encourage students to wash their hands after handling soil.

## 2. Guide the Procedure

- For best results, set the plants in a sunny place that is handy for watering.

- Group members can brainstorm predictions and rank them from the most likely to the least likely before deciding which one to record.

 Students can record their predictions and answer questions on *Science Notebook* p. 193.

 You may wish to have students use the CD-ROM Spreadsheet to organize and display information about when the seeds in each cup germinated.

## 3. Assess Performance

### Process Skills Checklist

- Did students **observe** differences in growth between seeds watered with tap water and with vinegar?

- Could students **identify the variable** they were testing? Did they understand that using vinegar simulates acid rain?

- Did students' **hypotheses** help explain their observations? Did they correlate the adverse effects of vinegar on seed germination with those of acid rain on plant growth?

### Analyze and Conclude

**1.** Results may vary, but the seeds should grow best in the cup watered with tap water. Students should hypothesize that the vinegar caused the differences in seed growth.

**2.** Students should infer that acid rain would harm plants by interfering with their growth.

# Water Worries

**Preview** *Students focus on how water becomes polluted and how pollution and a growing demand for water make clean water an increasingly valuable resource.*

## 1. Get Ready

### Science Terms acid rain, polluted

### Background

- All bodies of water, small and large, can become polluted. Even the mighty Mississippi River, 3,760 km (2,350 mi) long, could not withstand the assault of pollution. For many years, communities along the Mississippi dumped their wastes into the river because they assumed that such an immense body of water would clean itself. Conditions on the river have improved since the passage of the Clean Water Act in 1972, but problems remain. Although little sewage is now dumped into the river, harmful chemicals, some of them cancer-causing, have become trapped in river sediments and concentrated in river organisms. Such contaminants can poison the water for a long, long time. Twenty years after DDT was banned in the United States, water-quality researchers still find this deadly pesticide in Mississippi River water.

### Discussion Starter

- **Where does your drinking water come from? Why do you think it's safe to drink?** Sources of drinking water may vary, but most have been treated to make them safe to drink.

- **Can you drink the water directly from a local lake or river? Why?** Water from local sources is often too polluted for drinking without treatment.

- **Where does water pollution come from?** Trash, chemicals, sewage, and so on

- Use **Transparency 22,** "Water Worries," to initiate discussion about water pollution.

### Responding to Individual Needs

**Gifted and Talented Activity** Students can read *Acid Rain* by Michael Bright (Aladdin Books, 1991) to find out about the causes of acid rain, its effects on living things, and ways to reduce it. Let students summarize their findings in a presentation of their choice.

# Water Worries

You have been hired to solve the mystery of a polluted (pə loot′əd) river. A body of water that is **polluted** contains unwanted or harmful materials. Find out where the harmful materials, called pollutants, are coming from. How many ways are pollutants getting into the river?

## Investigate Further

### Integrating the Sciences

LIFE SCIENCE **What to Do** Explain that pollutants, such as some of the chemicals found in weed killers and insecticides, can build up in organisms. Tiny water plants and animals take in harmful chemicals from the water around them. When small fish eat these plants and animals, they take in the chemicals too. When larger fish eat the smaller fish, the chemicals build up in their bodies. People or other animals that eat these fish may also be harmed by the chemicals.

**What's the Result?** Students can draw the animals and plants that make up a simple food web in a body of water. Encourage them to explain how harmful chemicals could enter the water and be passed along from organism to organism.

How many of these causes of river pollution did you find?

**FARMING CHEMICALS** A farmer has been using fertilizers to grow better crops. The farmer has also been using chemicals to kill weeds and insects. When it rains, these materials are carried by the rain into the river.

**FACTORY WASTES** What happens to the waste water coming from the factory? Notice the smoke coming from the chimneys. Smoke can combine with moisture in the air to form **acid rain**. Recall what happened to plant growth in the activity on pages D56 and D57. What might happen to plants and animals in the river if acid rain falls into it?

**YARD CHEMICALS** Find the family doing yardwork. Fertilizers and chemicals used to kill insects and weeds can mix with rainwater and seep into the river.

**LEAKING GAS TANK** There's an old gas station, no longer in business, next to the factory. Gasoline is leaking from the underground tank that is cracked. Where will the gasoline go?

**LEAKING SEPTIC TANK** The school has an old septic tank buried underground. Septic tanks are containers that hold waste water from sinks and toilets. Old septic tanks often crack and leak. When they do, the waste water moves through the soil to the river.

**OIL CHANGE** Find the person changing the oil in a truck. If the oil is poured on the ground or down a drain, it will seep into the river.

**TOWN DUMP** Look at the town dump. Trash from the town is dumped into a hole in the ground. When it rains, the rainwater mixes with substances, such as battery acids, paints, and cleaners, in the trash. This polluted rainwater also flows into the river.

D59

## Integrating the Sciences

*PHYSICAL SCIENCE*

**What to Do** Explain that one reason water is so easily polluted is that so many things dissolve (seem to disappear) in it. Help students set up an experiment in which they try to dissolve a variety of substances, such as salt, soil, sand, instant coffee, and detergent in water.

**What's the Result?** Students should rate the materials according to how easily they dissolved in the water and record the results in chart form. ◆ **Does everything dissolve in water?** No. **What doesn't?** Pebbles, sticks, and grains of sand will drop out of the water.

 Have students use the CD-ROM Spreadsheet to chart their results.

# 2. Guide the Discussion

*Choose from the following strategies to facilitate discussion.*

## Drawing Conclusions

◆ **Why is it important to figure out where pollution is coming from?** So that people can find ways to stop the different types of pollution

◆ **What might happen if you ate fish from a polluted river?** Encourage speculation about the ways pollution might affect the fish and the animals or people that eat them.

## Connecting to the Activities

- *Not-So-Gentle Rain, p. D56*
  **How did you make acid rain in *Not-So-Gentle Rain*?** By using vinegar. **What causes acid rain in the real world?** Chemicals combine with moisture in the air to produce acid rain.

## Identifying and Solving Problems

- For each example of pollution shown in the illustration, ask: **What are some possible ways to stop or reduce the pollution?** Possible answers: farm—reduce use of chemicals and substitute natural materials such as compost, and plow horizontally with the river to decrease runoff; factory—use filters to clean chemicals from smoke, and clean and filter liquid pollutants before putting them into the river; gas station—pump gas out of leaking tanks and repair or remove them; septic tanks—pump them out and repair or replace them; motor oil—take used oil to designated facility for safe disposal; town dump—line dump with waterproof material or build a sanitary land fill farther from the river.

## 👤 Responding to Individual Needs

**Auditory Activity** Let students work in pairs. One student can read the text aloud while both students work together to examine the illustration and answer the questions. For students who have reading disabilities, tape recordings could be made by volunteers. Then students can listen to headphones of the textbook while following along with the rest of the class.

## Analyzing Data

**What kinds of pollutants have made their way into the oceans?** Sewage, plastics, oil, and chemicals from factories and farms

**What problems are caused by ocean pollution?** Pollution harms the living things in the oceans. It is a danger to people who swim in the ocean or eat food from it.

**If the oceans are so big, how have they become polluted?** There are more and more people on Earth each year dumping more and more pollutants into the ocean; there are more harmful chemicals being dumped into the oceans.

## Identifying and Solving Problems

* **How have people tried to stop water pollution?** By making it illegal to dump pollutants into rivers, lakes, and oceans.

### SCIENCE IN LITERATURE

*Drip Drop: Water's Journey* *
by Eve and Albert Stwertka
Along with the poster tips, students can make a list of ways they can save water at home and discuss these with their families.

*Available in the Trade Book Library.

### Salty-Water Worries

The pollution of rivers is only one of our "water worries." Oceans get polluted, too. People once thought that the oceans were so big that sewage or trash dumped into them wouldn't hurt them. But these things *have* harmed the oceans.

In the past, trash and sewage were hauled to and dumped into the oceans. It is now against the law in the United States to dump waste in the oceans. But trash and sewage are still dumped into oceans in many parts of the world.

Scientists have studied the oceans and found that sewage was the worst pollutant. Next came plastics, oil, and chemicals from factories and farms. These pollutants often flowed into rivers first, then they flowed out to the ocean. But these pollutants often washed back up on shore, making swimming at some beaches dangerous.

Over the years, many laws have been passed to prevent dumping of pollutants into rivers, lakes, and oceans. These bodies of water are much cleaner today than they were even a few years ago.

### Running Dry

Cleaning up water pollution isn't our only water worry. Having

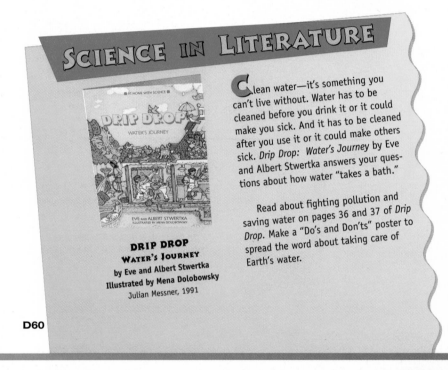

### SCIENCE IN LITERATURE

Clean water—it's something you can't live without. Water has to be cleaned before you drink it or it could make you sick. And it has to be cleaned after you use it or it could make others sick. *Drip Drop: Water's Journey* by Eve and Albert Stwertka answers your questions about how water "takes a bath."

Read about fighting pollution and saving water on pages 36 and 37 of *Drip Drop.* Make a "Do's and Don'ts" poster to spread the word about taking care of Earth's water.

**DRIP DROP**
**WATER'S JOURNEY**
by Eve and Albert Stwertka
Illustrated by Mena Dolobowsky
Julian Messner, 1991

**D60**

## Integrating the Curriculum

### Science & Language Arts

*WRITING LAWS* **What to Do** Remind students that many laws make it illegal to dump pollutants into rivers, lakes, and oceans. Ask them to pretend that they are lawmakers and to write and illustrate some laws to protect our water resources.

**What's the Result?** Which of your laws do you think would be easy for officials to enforce? Which do you think would be difficult? Accept all answers that show an understanding of how difficult enforcing some laws can be.

**Multi-Age Classroom** Group students so that those who are adept at writing are paired with those displaying artistic ability.

 Have students use the CD-ROM Painter and Writer to write and illustrate the laws.

▲ **In Rajasthan, India, drinking water is often scarce.**

enough fresh water for everyone is also a worry. Will there always be enough water for all the ways people need water?

The worry about running out of water is very real in some parts of the United States. People who use water from the Ogallala Aquifer, shown below, are especially worried. Scientists estimate that the water remaining in the aquifer will last only about 40 more years. In the southwestern corner of Kansas, the aquifer level has dropped about 60 m (200 ft) in the last 45 years. Plans to save water must be put into place now if there is to be fresh water in the future.

In Beijing, China, the groundwater level is dropping at such a fast rate that one third of the city's wells have gone dry. Two hundred major cities in China have water shortages.

During dry seasons, Madras, India, opens only one public water tap. To save water, the city opens the tap only between 4 A.M. and 6 A.M.

Water shouldn't be taken for granted. It should be treated as the valuable natural resource that it is. If we keep water supplies clean and use water wisely, we can have a future that is free from water worries. ■

**Does the Ogallala Aquifer supply your state with water?** ▼

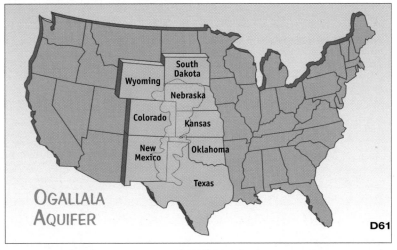

OGALLALA AQUIFER

D61

## Investigate Further

### Science, Technology & Society

**What to Do** Explain to students that xeriscaping is a type of landscaping which uses plants with low water needs. Students can create xeriscapes by planting cactuses or succulents in shallow clay dishes. Students could set up an experiment in which they grow grass in another dish and compare the water needs of grass and the xeriscape plants. Encourage students to find out where growing xeriscape plants would be most useful.

**What's the Result?** Students will discover that using plants with low water needs as ground cover can cut water use by half. Xeriscaping is becoming more common in dry regions like the American southwest.

**Multi-Age Classroom** Students can plant and care for the gardens in pairs.

## Identifying and Solving Problems

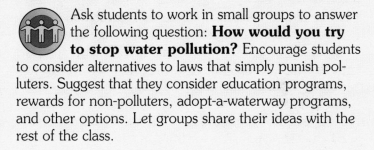 **How might people in the southwestern United States help solve their water problem?** By using less water at home, growing crops that need less water, and reusing waste water.

## Drawing Conclusions

**What might happen if people don't treat water as a valuable resource?** The supply of clean water won't keep up with the demand; we may have to pay a lot for water; more parts of the world may become uninhabitable.

## 3. Assess Understanding

Ask students to work in small groups to answer the following question: **How would you try to stop water pollution?** Encourage students to consider alternatives to laws that simply punish polluters. Suggest that they consider education programs, rewards for non-polluters, adopt-a-waterway programs, and other options. Let groups share their ideas with the rest of the class.

# Industrial-Revolution Pollution

**Preview** *Students focus on how industrialization has contributed to the pollution problem and how people have tried to stop pollution.*

## 1. Get Ready

### Background

- In the earliest days of the Industrial Revolution in Great Britain, the effects of acid rain were already apparent. In 1872, Robert Smith, an English chemist, published *Air and Rain,* in which he wrote of this new pollutant. Smith had observed damage to buildings and plants where coal-burning factories were located. He speculated that emissions from the factories created an acid responsible for the damage.

### Discussion Starter

**Why is pollution such a big problem today?** Changes over 500 years in industrialization and population have greatly added to the problem.

## 2. Guide the Discussion

*Choose from the following strategies to facilitate discussion.*

### Connecting to the Activities

- ***Not So Gentle Rain, p. D56***
  **What are the sources of acid rain in the real world?** Machines, factories and power plants that burn coal and oil, vehicle exhaust

### Responding to Individual Needs

**Students Acquiring English** As you point to each date on the time line on pp. D62–D63, read what is written. Help students reread the information.

## 3. Assess Understanding

Have students work in small groups to come up with time line entries for the next 50 years. Each entry should include future pollution problems and possible solutions.

# Industrial-Revolution Pollution

Since people first lived in communities, they have been polluting their environment. But pollution has become much more serious in modern times. That's because there are so many more people on Earth today than ever before.

The time line shows some events of the past that have made people's lives easier. It also presents some of the harmful effects that these events have led to, such as water pollution. As you read the time line, look for things that people have done to stop pollution.

**First Clean Water Act is passed by Congress.** Cleanup of lakes and rivers begin. **1948**

**Thomas A. Edison invents the electric light bulb.** Electricity is produced by burning coal and fuel oil. More air pollution and acid rain result. **1879**

**Industrial Revolution begins in England, moves to America.** New machines are invented and many factories are built. The machines burn coal that pollutes the air, causing acid rain. More people move to cities, so more sewage and trash are released into rivers. **1750**

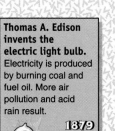

**1859 E.L. Drake drills the first oil well in Pennsylvania.** Oil is later refined to make products such as gasoline. When burned, gasoline puts pollutants into the air.

**D62**

# Integrating the Curriculum

## Science & the Arts

**What to Do** Ask students to think about what the future will be like. Will the world be a healthy place to live or will it be polluted? Suggest that students draw two pictures side by side, contrasting what the world will be like if people don't reduce pollution and what it will be like if they do.

**What's the Result?** Students can use their drawings for a bulletin board display.

**Multi-Age Classroom** Let a group of three or four students work together. Encourage them to discuss the causes and visible effects of pollution before they begin their pictures.

 Have students use the CD-ROM Painter to draw their pictures.

**United States and Canada pledge to control air pollution.** Both countries agree to develop ways to decrease acid rain.
**1980**

**The Environmental Protection Agency (EPA) is formed.** This U.S. government agency was given the job of setting standards for water quality.
**1971**

**1992**
**Safe Drinking Water Act adds standards.** Standards are set to control 24 other water pollutants from getting into drinking water.

**1974**
**The Safe Drinking Water Act is passed by Congress.** This act sets limits for the amount of germs and chemicals allowed in drinking water.

**1970**
**First Earth Day** Congress declares April 22 Earth Day so that people become aware of air, water, and land pollution.

You can see that many things have happened to help improve the environment and reduce pollution. More still needs to be done. What will be the time line for the future? ■

---

**INVESTIGATION 1**

**1.** What kinds of water worries could the people of your city or town be having?

**2.** Write a story about what life will be like 100 years from now. Tell whether there will still be water pollution and water worries. What solutions will have been found?

D63

# Assessment

## Portfolio
### Write a Letter to the Editor
Students can identify a pollution problem in the community and write a letter to the editor about it. Encourage students to describe the problem in detail and to suggest possible solutions.

Have students use the CD-ROM Writer to write their letters.

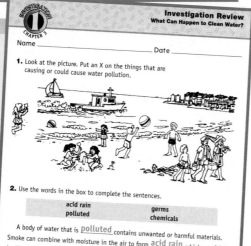

**Investigation Review**
**What Can Happen to Clean Water?**

Name _____ Date _____

**1.** Look at the picture. Put an X on the things that are causing or could cause water pollution.

**2.** Use the words in the box to complete the sentences.

| acid rain | germs |
| polluted | chemicals |

A body of water that is <u>polluted</u> contains unwanted or harmful materials. Smoke can combine with moisture in the air to form <u>acid rain</u> which can fall in bodies of water. The Safe Drinking Water Act passed by Congress sets limits for the amount of <u>germs</u> and <u>chemicals</u> allowed in drinking water.

Sample questions are: Are there factories nearby dumping waste water into the river or polluting air, and therefore causing acid rain? Are there farms near the river where farmers use pesticides and fertilizers?

**Process Skills**
*Identifying Variables, Making a Hypothesis*
Your cousin asks you why the fish are dying in a river near his house. What might you ask him before you form a hypothesis? Write the questions on a separate sheet of paper.

---

# Close
## the Investigation

**Critical Thinking Skills**
Evaluating, Generating Ideas, Expressing Ideas, Solving Problems

**1.** People might worry about their water supply becoming polluted or running out.

**2.** Students' stories should reflect the understanding that unless pollution of water resources is stopped, the pollution problems 100 years from now will be worse.

**Challenge** Have the class write to a local office of the Environmental Protection Agency for information about what the EPA does. If an EPA representative is available, students might interview him or her to find out more about this agency's role in reducing pollution.

## Following Up

**Baseline Assessment** Return to the list of possible sources of pollution students made at the beginning of the investigation. Ask students what changes they would like to make in the list based on what they have learned. Then discuss what is being done to reduce pollution from each source listed.

**Reteaching** Use the illustration on pp. D58–D59 and models of two rivers to help students understand how pollution affects a waterway. You will need two clear plastic shoe boxes, water, and several different "pollutants." For instance, you could use different solution of colored water to represent agricultural chemicals, vinegar for acid rain, colored mineral oil for gasoline and motor oil, and dirt and paper debris for trash. As you read through the captions on the illustration, add (or let students add) the appropriate type of pollution to one shoe box of water. Then help students compare the two "rivers."

Use *Science Notebook* p. 195.

◄ **Investigation Review**
Use Investigation Review p. 94 in the *Assessment Guide.*

# HOW DOES WATER POLLUTION MOVE FROM PLACE TO PLACE?

## Planner

**Subconcept** Water pollution that reaches, or is released into, the ocean is dispersed by tides and currents.

### Objectives

- **Observe** how tides and currents can move pollution.
- **Describe** the effects of water pollution and **investigate** efforts to control it.

**Pacing** 2–3 class periods

**Science Terms** current, tides

## Activate Prior Knowledge

**Baseline Assessment** Ask: **What kinds of things might you see on an ocean beach? Where did they come from? How did they get there?** Record responses for use in Following Up.

## Activity All Washed Up

**Preview** *Students make a model of a coast and tides. They should find that their model tides carry the "pollution" up on to the coast.*

## 1. Get Ready

**Time** about 30 minutes

**Grouping** groups of 3–4

**Collaborative Strategy** One student can raise and lower the pan while other students observe the effects.

**Safety** Review safety precautions with students. Make sure students wear goggles during this activity and clean up any spills immediately to prevent accidents.

---

# HOW DOES WATER POLLUTION MOVE FROM PLACE TO PLACE?

You saw in Investigation 1 that pollution dumped on land can end up in the water. In this investigation you'll see how water can move that pollution from place to place.

## Activity

### All Washed Up

*Tides are the daily rise and fall of ocean water. If you've ever visited an ocean beach, you know what tides do. In this activity you'll make a model to see if tides add to pollution along coastlines.*

**MATERIALS**
- goggles
- rocks, gravel, or sand
- large baking pan
- water
- metric ruler
- potting soil
- spoon
- cooking oil
- *Science Notebook*

**SAFETY**
Wear goggles during this activity. Clean up any spills immediately. Wash your hands when you have finished this activity.

### Procedure

1. **Make a model** of an ocean coastline, using rocks, gravel, or sand. Put the material you have chosen in one end of a baking pan. Arrange the materials to look like a beach or rocky coast.

2. **Pour water** into the pan until the water is 1 cm deep. Sprinkle a little soil on your "ocean." Then add one spoonful of cooking oil.

D64

## Investigate Further

### Experiment

**What to Do** Have students develop an experiment modeling how oil spills might be cleaned up. They can use the model coastlines they created in All Washed Up. Provide them with a variety of materials to use for cleaning up the spill, including cooking oil, cosmetic puffs, dry oatmeal, bread, detergent, plastic foam, and strainers. Students can present the results of their plan to the class in a report or a drawing. Encourage students to research methods that have already been tried to clean up the results of marine oil spills. Have students record their findings on *Science Notebook* p. 197.

**What's the Result?** Students will discover that spilled oil is very difficult to remove from the surface of water and the surrounding coastline.

**Step 3**

**3.** Talk with your group and predict what effect moving the water up onto the "coast" will have on your coastline materials. Explain why you made the prediction you did. Record your prediction in your *Science Notebook*. Then slowly raise the ocean end of the pan until the water moves up onto the coast. Slowly lower the pan. Do this three or four times.

**4.** Now observe your coastline materials. Touch them. Record your observations.

### Analyze and Conclude

**1.** How did your model represent the motion of tides on Earth?

**2.** What did you observe in step 4 when you looked at and touched your coastline materials? Compare this result with your prediction.

**3.** The materials you put into your ocean are a model of pollution from oil spills and the dumping of wastes. What can you infer from your model about how ocean pollution affects land?

D65

## Responding to Individual Needs

**Students Acquiring English** Students could work in groups and make "before and after" drawings of their coastlines to show the effects of tides on water pollution. Display the drawings in the classroom. Invite students to describe in English what is happening in each drawing.

 Have students use the CD-ROM Painter to create their drawings.

## 2. Guide the Procedure

• Make sure students raise and lower the pan slowly and gently so that they can observe the changes that occur.

• Encourage students to discuss their observations so that everyone in the group is in agreement as to what happened.

 Students can record their predictions and answer questions on *Science Notebook* pp. 196–197.

 You may suggest that students use the CD-ROM Painter to create drawings showing the results of this activity.

## 3. Assess Performance

### Process Skills Checklist

• Did students carefully follow directions when **making** their **model** coastlines?

• Were students' **inferences** based on their observations during the activity as well as prior knowledge? Did students recognize that water can carry pollutants on to land?

### Analyze and Conclude

**1.** Raising and lowering the pan represented the rise and fall of the tides.

**2.** The coastline materials have soil and cooking oil on them. Predictions may vary but the materials should be sticky and may be difficult to remove from hands.

**3.** Tides can carry some forms of pollution up on to the land.

# Activity Going My Way?

**Preview** *Students observe how cold water and hot water interact to form currents and infer what causes similar currents in the ocean. Students should find that the hot water is forced upward as the cooler, more dense surrounding water sinks, creating a current.*

## 1. Get Ready

**Time** about 30 minutes

**Grouping** groups of 3–4

**Multi-Age Strategy** Students who are adept at measuring can help others do their measurements.

**Materials Hints** If the small jar floats, put small clean pebbles in the bottom to weigh it down. Glass baby-food jars work better, but they break easily and are more dangerous.

**Safety** Review safety precautions with students. Clean up all spills immediately to prevent accidents.

## 2. Guide the Procedure

- Remind students to try not to disturb the water as they remove the lid from the jar.

Students can record their predictions and answer questions on *Science Notebook* pp. 198–199.

Students can use the CD-ROM Painter to create diagrams showing the currents of hot and cold water.

## 3. Assess Performance

### Process Skills Checklist

- Were students' **predictions** based on past experiences and observations? Did they remember that moving water can carry pollutants?
- Did students make accurate **observations** of the movement of the food-coloring "currents"?
- Were students' **inferences** based on their observations? Did they understand that pollutants can be carried along by currents?

### Analyze and Conclude

1. The colored (hot) water rises. The cold water sinks.
2. Pollutants could be carried along by these currents or "rivers" of water.

# Activity

## Going My Way?

***Tides move ocean water. "Rivers" of water called currents also move through the oceans. How might currents move pollution from place to place?***

**MATERIALS**

- goggles
- cold tap water
- clear plastic aquarium
- dropper
- food coloring
- small jar with lid
- hot tap water
- ***Science Notebook***

**SAFETY**

Wear goggles during this activity. Take care when using hot water so you don't burn your skin. Clean up any spills immediately.

### Procedure

**1.** Pour cold water into a clear plastic aquarium until the aquarium is three-fourths filled.

**2.** Put three drops of food coloring into a small jar. Carefully fill the jar with hot tap water. Screw on the lid.

**3.** Slowly place the jar upright on the bottom of the aquarium. Try not to disturb the water. **Talk with your group** and **predict** what will happen when you take the lid off the jar. Explain why you made the prediction you did. **Record** your prediction in your *Science Notebook*.

**4.** Slowly remove the lid of the jar. **Observe** and **record** what happens.

### Analyze and Conclude

**1.** What happened after you took off the lid? In which direction did the hot colored water move? In which direction did the cold water move?

**2.** You made a model of one way that water moves near coastlines. **Hypothesize** what would happen to pollutants that get swept into a current.

D66

## Responding to Individual Needs

**Visual/Spatial Activity** To see if students understand the concepts in Going My Way, ask them to make a diagram with arrows explaining what the experiment showed.

**Multi-Age Classroom** Working in small groups, students can collaborate on the diagrams. **What do you think happens when hot air and cold air meet?** The cold air sinks and the hot air rises and you get strong winds, and possibly also storms. Encourage interested students to watch a weather report on TV.

Have students research ocean currents using the Ocean Currents Data Pack on the CD-ROM.

# The Current Idea

On January 10, 1992, a ship carrying 7,250 bathtub toys lost its cargo during a storm in the northern Pacific Ocean. Knowing where the toys washed ashore helped scientists learn a little more about the path that ocean pollution takes.

## A "River" in the Ocean

Ocean pollution is moved around the world by the constant motion of the water. Currents are important water movers.

A **current** is a narrow, fast-moving "river" of water in the ocean.

Currents at the ocean's surface are kept in motion by winds that blow steadily in one direction. When surface currents get close to land, they curve away from it and change direction.

Look at the map of world ocean currents. The **X** shows where the ship lost its cargo. Predict where the bathtub toys washed ashore.

So far, more than 400 bathtub toys have been found along the Alaskan shoreline. Scientists are waiting to see if more toys will wash ashore elsewhere.

**The major ocean surface currents ▼**

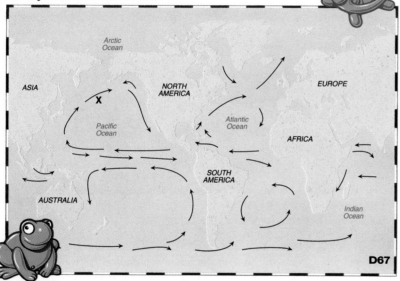

Arctic Ocean

ASIA

NORTH AMERICA

EUROPE

Pacific Ocean

Atlantic Ocean

AFRICA

SOUTH AMERICA

AUSTRALIA

Indian Ocean

D67

# Integrating the Curriculum

## Science & the Arts

**COMPOSING**

**What to Do** Oceans and water have long held a fascination for songwriters. Ask students to think of as many songs about the ocean as they can. Then ask them to write a new song about the ocean, or to write new words to a song they already know.

**What's the Result?** Students can sing or play their songs for the class if they wish.

**Multi-Age Classroom** Students can work together in small groups to write and perform their songs.

---

# The Current Idea

**Preview** *Students focus on what causes waves, tides, and currents, and how such movements of ocean water can carry pollution around the world.*

## 1. Get Ready

### Science Terms  current, tides

### Background

- The rising and falling ocean tides are caused by the interaction of Earth, the Moon, and, to a lesser degree, the Sun. The Moon's gravitational force is primarily responsible. The pull of the Moon's gravity on Earth's oceans causes a bulge of water to appear on the side of Earth nearest the Moon and a similar but smaller bulge to appear on the opposite side of Earth. Since Earth is rotating and the Moon is orbiting Earth, in most places high tides occur twice during a period of 24 hours and 50 minutes. The Sun also exerts a gravitational pull on Earth's oceans, but it is so far from Earth that its effect is somewhat less than half that of the Moon. The Sun's gravitational pull can either add to or reduce the Moon's pull, depending on how Earth, the Sun, and the Moon are aligned.

### Discussion Starter

- **If you put a message in a sealed bottle and dropped the bottle into the ocean, where do you think it would end up?** Encourage students to give reasons for their predictions.

- Show students a map of the Pacific rim. Point out the countries along the rim and have students find Alaska. On the Pacific coast of the northwestern United States, people sometimes find glass floats, used by Japanese fishing boats, washed up on shore. Ask: **How do you think these floats got from Japan to the United States?** Encourage students to speculate about how the movements of the water might carry things across an ocean. Suggest that they think back to the results of All Washed Up and Going My Way.

## 2. Guide the Discussion

*Choose from the following strategies to facilitate discussion.*

 **Responding to Individual Needs**

**Students Acquiring English** Students can create visual dictionaries of the key terms presented in this resource. An entry should consist of the term in English and the student's native language, a drawing to explain it, and an English sentence using each term. As students view the completed project, encourage them to pronounce the terms in both languages.

Suggest students use the CD-ROM Painter and Writer to create their dictionaries.

### Drawing Conclusions

- **Is the Moon's gravity weaker or stronger than Earth's gravity?** Weaker

- **What might happen if the Moon's gravity were stronger than Earth's gravity?** Earth might be pulled closer to the Moon or orbit it. The tides might be pulled even higher.

- **Why do the tides go up and down?** Because sea water is free to move, the Moon's gravity pulls it into a bulge toward the Moon. A similar bulge is created on the opposite side of Earth. As Earth turns on its axis, the Moon orbits Earth, carrying the tidal bulges along with it. Students can demonstrate the movements of Earth and the Moon using a softball and a ping pong ball.

### Connecting to the Activities

- *All Washed Up, p. D64*
  **How did you create tides in All Washed Up?** By raising and lowering a pan of water **What happened to the water pollution in the activity?** The tides carried it on to the shore.

- **How might pollution carried by tides affect land plants and animals?** As it washes up on shore, it might harm them.

- *Going My Way, p. D66*
  **Remembering what you observed during Going My Way, where would you expect rising ocean currents?** Near the Equator **Where would you expect sinking ocean currents?** Near the poles

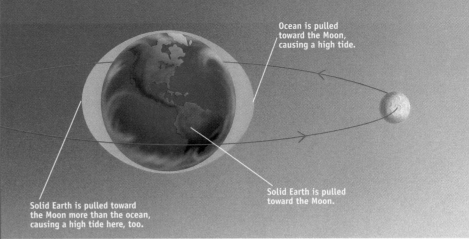

Ocean is pulled toward the Moon, causing a high tide.

Solid Earth is pulled toward the Moon more than the ocean, causing a high tide here, too.

Solid Earth is pulled toward the Moon.

▲ As Earth turns, the tides rise and fall.

**These Currents Run Deep**

The currents that moved the floating bathtub toys are surface currents. There are also currents deeper in the ocean. Deep ocean currents are caused by differences in water temperature.

In the activity on page D66, you saw that warm water rises and that cold water sinks and takes its place. This is similar to the way deep ocean currents move. Ocean waters are warm near the equator (ē kwāt′ər) and cold near the poles. So ocean waters tend to rise near the equator and sink near the poles. This steady movement of water results in ocean currents.

**Ocean Ups and Downs**

If you've ever spent a day at the ocean shore, you may have noticed that waves move in closer to shore, and then move back out again. This motion of the water is called tides. **Tides** are the daily rise and fall of ocean water. Tides helped move some of the lost bathtub toys onto shore.

Tides are caused by both gravity (grav′i tē) and by Earth's rotation, or spinning. Gravity is the pull that all things have on one another. Earth's gravity keeps us on Earth. Earth's gravity also keeps the Moon close to Earth.

The Moon has gravity, too. As the Moon circles Earth, the Moon's gravity pulls on Earth. This pull causes the Earth's oceans to move outward toward the Moon. As Earth rotates, or spins, different parts of the oceans receive the greatest pull of the Moon.

**D68**

## Investigate Further

### Cultural Connection

**OCEAN CURRENTS** **What to Do** Explain that ocean currents were first observed by sailors. In 1492, Christopher Columbus sailed west from Spain. Trade winds and ocean currents carried his ships. Ask a student to put a bottle cap at one end of a long tray. Help another student slowly pour water in the tray at the same end.
**What's the Result?** **What happened to the cap?** The water carried it forward. **What happened as the water hit the other end?** It pushed the cap back again. Students can try blowing on the cap while the water is poured. On a globe, help them trace the Equatorial Current and the Gulf Stream.

**High tide (*left*) and low tide (*right*) in Gloucester, Massachusetts**

**Pollution Goes for a Ride**

Tides and currents move polluted ocean water from one place to another. More often than not, pollutants wash back up on the shore near the place they came from. Think back to how oil affected the shoreline you made in the activity on pages D64 and D65. You used cooking oil to pollute the water. The tides you made moved the pollution back up on the shore.

One source of ocean pollution is oil spills. Strong storms at sea can cause oil tankers to break apart. When they do break apart, oil spills out and floats on the ocean's surface. The oil kills animals that live in or near the ocean, and it ruins beaches. You probably wouldn't be too upset to find bathtub toys on a beach. But if you were to find oil covering the sand, it's likely that wouldn't make you very happy.

Although pollution can sometimes be traced to a country or a private company, the oceans belong to the whole world. So the problem of ocean pollution can be solved only when all countries of the world work together. ■

### UNIT PROJECT LINK

Waterville's town officials want to protect their water supply. They want to produce a 12-month calendar. Each month will carry a message about how to protect the town's water from pollution and suggest ways to conserve water. Write twelve messages and create a "Conserve and Care" calendar that each school and family in Waterville will want to use.

D69

## Unit Project Link

Students should begin by brainstorming a list of the twelve best messages about how to protect Waterville's water supply from pollution and how water can be conserved in Waterville. Encourage students to record their message possibilities in their *Science Notebooks* on p. 200. Groups should decide which twelve messages they will include in their "Conserve and Care" calendars. Then students should use Unit Project Master D6 (TRB p. 69) to begin constructing their calendars. Encourage students to illustrate their messages.

## Making Inferences

 **Why do the currents move in a circle around the Atlantic Ocean?** Because they hit land, which changes their direction. Show students this phenomenon on a world map.

**How could you find out if pollution moves from place to place in the oceans?** Follow or track the course of objects floating in the ocean.

## Analyzing Data

• **So far, 400 rubber ducks, turtles, and other bathtub toys have been found along 300 km (about 500 mi) of Alaskan shoreline. Where do you think other toys may be washed ashore?** The toys may wash up along the western coastline of the United States. Note: In an updated news story, oceanographers said that winds pushed some of the toys north through the polar ice cap. They predict that some toys may wash up on the shores of Iceland, Norway, and Great Britain after the turn of the century.

## Identifying and Solving Problems

**What are some of the harmful effects of ocean pollution?** Pollution harms the plants and animals that live in or near the ocean. It also harms people who swim in polluted water or eat contaminated food from the sea. Pollution can spread around the world in ocean waters for many years to come.

## 3. Assess Understanding

Students can work in groups of three or four. Have them imagine that there has been an oil spill off the western coast of northern Africa. Encourage them to use the world map on p. D67 to predict where the spill will spread. Remind them to think about all the types of ocean water movements they have studied: waves, tides, and currents. Invite students to share their predictions and reasoning with the rest of the class.

# Mother of Waters

**Preview** *Students focus on the pollution and cleanup of the Chesapeake Bay.*

## 1. Get Ready

### Background

- More than 40 rivers and streams flow into Chesapeake Bay and form the Chesapeake watershed, a 64,000 square-mile area. In the past 50 years, the bay region population has doubled. Resulting development has removed many forests, fields, and marshlands that helped filter water pollution. Saving the Bay involves controlling pollution, limiting fishing, and restoring natural protection.

### Discussion Starter

 **How can you tell if water is polluted or not?** The health and number of living things in the water provide clues to how clean or polluted the water is.

## 2. Guide the Discussion

*Choose from the following strategies to facilitate discussion.*

### Making Comparisons

- **How is an estuary different from a river or an ocean?** A river has fresh water. An ocean has salt water. In an estuary, fresh water mixes with salt water.

### Connecting to the Activities

- ***All Washed Up, p. D64***
  **How might ocean pollution enter the Chesapeake Bay?** On the tides

### Drawing Conclusions

- **What caused organisms in Chesapeake Bay to begin dying out?** Increased pollution and overfishing

## 3. Assess Understanding

Encourage students to draw three pictures of Chesapeake Bay: before it was polluted, at its most polluted, and now, as it is cleaner.

# Mother of Waters

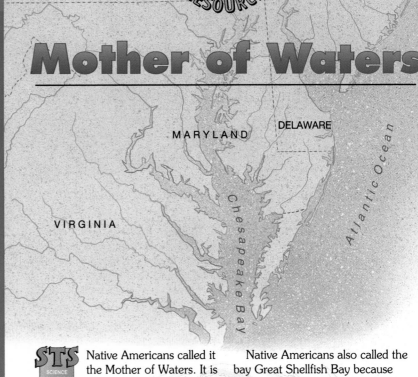

MARYLAND

DELAWARE

Atlantic Ocean

VIRGINIA

Chesapeake Bay

 Native Americans called it the Mother of Waters. It is 320 km (200 mi) long, it stretches over 12,800 km (8,000 mi) of shoreline, and it has 150 rivers and streams flowing into it. What is it? It's the Chesapeake Bay.

The Chesapeake Bay is the nation's largest estuary (es'tyoo er ē). An estuary is a place where fresh water mixes with salt water. The Chesapeake Bay estuary is home to a great variety of life. It has more than 2,500 different kinds of plants and animals living in its waters and along its shore.

Native Americans also called the bay Great Shellfish Bay because there were so many crabs, clams, and oysters in there.

Many people enjoy eating shellfish, so for years the shellfish industry grew. Then something began to happen. The numbers of shellfish that were caught began to decrease.

There were two reasons for the decrease in shellfish in the estuary: pollution and people. Every stream and river that flowed past farms and factories picked up pollutants and carried them to the Chesapeake Bay. Over the years, 13 million

**D70**

# Integrating the Curriculum

## Science & Social Studies

 **What to Do** The rivers that flow into the Chesapeake Bay make up what is called the Chesapeake watershed. Suggest that students look at the map to find out which rivers make up the Chesapeake watershed and create a map showing what they've learned.

**What's the Result?** Encourage students to use their maps to explain how sewage dumped in a river such as the Susquehanna in Pennsylvania could affect the quality of water in the Chesapeake Bay.

**Multi-Age Classroom** Students can work in small groups to make their maps.

people moved to the land that drains into the bay. These people built towns. They produced sewage and trash. They also overfished the waters. All these things decreased the number of living things in the bay.

Then the federal Environmental Protection Agency (EPA) began a study of the bay. In 1983 they told the states that surround the bay how to save it. The farmers began planting crops in a way that lessened the runoff of fertilizers and chemicals into the bay. Sewage was treated, fishing was limited, and trash was placed in landfills.

Today the water of Chesapeake Bay is improved. In 1989 it was impossible to see down into the water more than 20 cm (8 in.). But today you can see down 46 cm (18 in.). Of course, there is a long way to go. The Native Americans could see to the bottom, 6 m (20 ft) deep!

Lessons learned from the Mother of Waters can be used to control—and prevent—water pollution around the world. ■

Oysters are once again plentiful in the Chesapeake Bay. ▼

--- INVESTIGATION 2 ---

1. Imagine walking on a beach on the east coast of southern Florida. You accidentally drop a ball into the ocean. Where might the ball go?

2. People used to think that the oceans were so big that anything could be dumped into them without harming them. Explain why this isn't so.

D71

## Assessment

### Portfolio
**Make a Concept Map**
Suggest that students summarize the main concepts of the investigation in the form of a concept map. Use the Activity Support Master, "Word Web", p. 46. Make sure they include the following words and phrases: ocean pollution, how it moves, the damage it does, currents, tides, and waves.

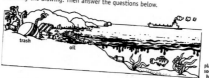

**Investigation Review**
**How Does Water Pollution Move From Place to Place?**

Name _____ Date _____

1. Circle the word that best completes each sentence.
   a. (Currents, Tides) can form as the wind blows over the surface of water.
   b. Steady winds that blow from one region of the world to another region cause (deep-ocean currents, surface currents).
   c. The moon pulls on Earth's surface, causing (tides, surface currents).
   d. When warm water rises and cold water sinks, (waves, deep-ocean currents) are formed.

2. Study the drawing. Then answer the questions below.

trash    oil    plastic & soda-can holder

   a. How did the oil get so far up on the beach and on the rocks?
   The tide carried the oil far up on the beach.

   b. Look at the plants growing on the bottom of the ocean floor. How did the plastic soda-can holder get from the beach to the plants?
   A wave or tide could move the holder into the ocean. It may have sunk on its own or currents may have moved it to the ocean floor.

**Process Skills**
*Observing*    Sample answers: good water visibility; healthy populations of organisms; no trash; no unpleasant smell to the water.
Suppose you could visit Chesapeake Bay. How could you tell that efforts at cleaning up Chesapeake Bay are working? Write your answer on a separate sheet of paper.

### Critical Thinking Skills
**Synthesizing, Applying**

1. The ball could go up the eastern coast of the United States. It could even go to Europe.

2. Currents, waves, and tides carry pollution around the world. Scientists have discovered that the ocean is not able to absorb or break up all the pollutants dumped into it.

**Challenge** Students can work in small groups to find out about any local waterways that have been threatened by pollution. **What were the sources of the pollution? How did the pollution affect the waterway and the things living in and around it? What was done to clean it up?**

### Following Up
**Baseline Assessment** Have students review the hypotheses they made when they began the investigation about how things move across the ocean. Let them change their hypotheses based on what they have learned.

**Reteaching** Work with students to create a series of illustrations for a slide show explaining the concepts of ocean pollution, how it spreads, and what damage it does.

Use *Science Notebook* p. 201.

◄ **Investigation Review**
Use Investigation Review p. 95 in the *Assessment Guide.*

# HOW CAN WE SAVE AND PROTECT WATER?

## Planner

**Subconcept** Water must be conserved—and pollution cleaned up and prevented—in order to insure that there is enough safe fresh water for everyone's basic needs.

### Objectives

- **Collect, record,** and **interpret** water use **data.**
- **Explain** why we must save and protect water and **identify** ways to do so.

**Pacing** 2–3 class periods

## Activate Prior Knowledge

**Baseline Assessment** Show students a gallon of water. Explain that this gallon represents all the water on Earth. Then show students two tablespoons of water and explain this represents all the available fresh liquid water on Earth. Ask: **How can we make sure that this is enough water for all the people on Earth?** Save students' ideas for use in Following Up.

---

The amount of water on Earth never changes. Yet the number of people on Earth is growing all the time. How can people protect and save this limited amount of water?

# Activity
## Down the Drain

**MATERIALS**
- *Science Notebook*

*How much water does your household use each day? Could you use less? Find out!*

---

### Procedure

In your *Science Notebook*, **record** each activity in which you or others in your home use water during one day. Use the table to see how much water each activity uses. Add up the number of gallons of water used for each activity. Then add up the amounts of water used the entire day.

| Water-Using Activity | Water (in gallons) |
|---|---|
| Bath | 25 |
| Ten-minute shower | 50 |
| Flush of the toilet | 5 |
| Faucet running to brush teeth | 2 |
| Faucet running to wash dishes | 30 |
| Dishwasher load | 10 |
| Washing machine load | 32 |

### Analyze and Conclude

What surprised you about how your household uses water? How could you use less water?

**D72**

---

# Activity
## Down the Drain

**Preview** *Students collect data about their household water use, and infer ways to reduce it. Students will probably be surprised by how much water their households use in one day.*

## 1. Get Ready

**Time** one day observing water use at home, then about 15 minutes in class

**Grouping** individual

## 2. Guide the Procedure

- Suggest that students list the water-using activities first and then record the number of times each activity is done in one day.

---

 Encourage students to record their numbers and answer questions on *Science Notebook* p. 202.

 You may recommend that students use the CD-ROM Spreadsheet to organize and display their data.

## 3. Assess Performance

### Process Skills Checklist

- Did students **collect data** about all water-using activities? Did they **record** their data accurately?
- Were students' **inferences** based on what they observed about water use? Did they understand how much of the water used daily is wasted?

### Analyze and Conclude

Students will probably be surprised by how much water their household uses in one day. Possible answers include taking a bath instead of a shower, or a shorter shower; shutting off the faucet while you brush your teeth; running the washing machine only when you have a full load of clothes.

# Activity
## Drops Count

*Find out just how much water goes down the drain, one drop at a time.*

### MATERIALS
- empty, small milk carton
- water
- graduate
- cup
- timer
- *Science Notebook*

### SAFETY
Clean up any spills immediately.

### Procedure

**1.** With a partner, predict how much water is wasted in 30 minutes by a dripping faucet. Record your prediction in your *Science Notebook*.

**2.** Use a milk carton as a model of a dripping faucet. Your teacher will make a hole in the bottom of the carton with a pin.

**3.** Hold your finger over the hole, and have your partner add water to the carton until it is full. Hold the carton above a graduate. Set a timer for one minute.

**4.** Remove your finger and let water drip from the hole for one minute. Then place the carton in a cup.

**5.** Measure and record the amount of water in the graduate.

Step 4

### Analyze and Conclude

**1.** How much water did you collect? Compute the amount of water that you could collect in 30 minutes.

**2.** Infer how a dripping faucet can become a big water waster over one year's time.

D73

---

## Responding to Individual Needs

**Auditory Activity** Suggest that students use the results of the activity as the basis for a song about saving water by fixing a leaky faucet. Let them record their songs and share them with the rest of the class.

**Multi-Age Classroom** Students can work in small groups to write and perform their songs.

---

# Activity  Drops Count

**Preview** *Students watch how a dripping faucet can waste water, record about how many drops of water are wasted in five minutes, and infer how a dripping faucet could become a big water-waster over a year's time.*

**Advance Preparation** *See p. D54b.*

## 1. Get Ready

**Time** about 30 minutes

**Grouping** pairs

 **Collaborative Strategy** One student can hold the carton above the measuring cup while the other counts the drops.

**Materials Hints** Use 1/2-pint milk cartons for this activity. Make a small hole in the bottom of each for the water to drip out.

**Safety** Review safety precautions with students. Clean up any spills immediately to prevent accidents.

## 2. Guide the Procedure

- To simulate a dripping faucet, make a small hole so drops of water come out one at a time.
- Before students do step 3, have them test their milk cartons to make sure the water drips at a steady pace.

 Encourage students to record their measurements and computations on *Science Notebook* p. 203.

 Suggest students use the CD-ROM Spreadsheet to organize and display their data.

## 3. Assess Performance

### Process Skills Checklist

- Did students carefully **collect** (count the drops) and **record** their **data**?
- Were students' **inferences** based on their computations of how much water is wasted in 30 minutes?

### Analyze and Conclude

1. Answers may vary but students should record data accurately and do the calculation carefully.
2. A dripping faucet can waste thousands of gallons of water in a year.

# Isn't Water Free?

**Preview** *Students focus on the cost of water and how water use is measured.*

## 1. Get Ready

### Background

- In the United States, we use lots of water. *Every day we use 137 billion gallons of water to irrigate our fields, and another 25 billion gallons a day for manufacturing.*

### Discussion Starter

- **In what ways do people use water every day?** Encourage students to consider water use in homes, factories, schools, and so on.
- **Where does that water come from?** Encourage students to share what they know about your community's water system.
- **Does it cost money? How do you know?** Ask students to give evidence to support their answers.

## 2. Guide the Discussion

*Choose from the following strategies to facilitate discussion.*

###  Responding to Individual Needs

**Students Acquiring English** Bring in several water bills to show students the cost of water in your area and how water use is measured. If possible, take students to examine the school's water meter. They might even take readings at the beginning and end of the week and then calculate how much water the school used during that time. Encourage students to compare the water systems in their native country with the community in which they now live.

---

# Isn't Water Free?

**STS** SCIENCE TECHNOLOGY & SOCIETY Imagine that you are eating in a restaurant with your family. You ask for a glass of water. When you get the bill for the meal, you see a $5.00 charge added for the water.

Charging this much for a glass of water may seem unfair. Isn't water free, after all, like air? In many areas of the world, water is not free. Many people in the United States already pay a water utility company for the water used in their homes. They're charged for every thousand gallons of water that they use.

### A Few Cents a Day

The average cost per thousand gallons of water in the United States is $1.65. This means that in some places, people pay less than $1.65 while in other places they pay more.

A thousand gallons is a lot of water. If you drank eight 8-oz glasses of water a day, a thousand gallons would last for over three and

**Most restaurants don't charge for water.** ▼

D74

---

## Investigate Further

**STS** **Science, Technology & Society**

WRITING GUIDES  **What to Do** Encourage students to create a class guide to water-friendly household cleansers. Other good resources are the books *50 Simple Things You Can Do to Save the Earth* by the Earthworks Group (Berkely: Earthworks Press, 1989) and *The Green Consumer* by John Elkington, Julia Hailes, and Joel Makower (Penguin Books, 1990). In addition many local environmental agencies have information about how to make and use less toxic household cleansers.

**What's the Result?** Students might publish their guides and make them available to other classes.

**Multi-Age Classroom** Students can work together in small groups to create their guides.

a half years. Getting this much water for $1.65 (or less than a penny per gallon) would amaze people in other countries. People who live on the island of Bermuda pay about $100.00 per thousand gallons of water.

**Keeping Track**

How do you know when you have used a thousand gallons of water? In places where people pay for water, each building has a water meter. A water meter, shown on the right, is a device that measures the amount of water that comes through a pipe into a home or business. The meter may be in the basement of an apartment building or mounted on the outside of a house.

▲ How many gallons of water have been used?

**A meter reader checks how many gallons of water were used.** ▼

Meter readers are people who work for water companies. They make regular visits to every building that has a water meter. They look at the numbers on the meters to see how much water has been used since the last time the meter was checked. The water company then sends a bill for the amount of water used.

The money that people pay to a water company covers the cost of treating water so that it's safe to drink. It also helps in paying to build and maintain the pipes that bring water into homes.

As the number of people in the world grows, more water will be needed. It may not be long before water supplies are so reduced that everyone will have to pay for water. And in some places, water may become very costly.

D75

**Connecting to the Activities**

- *Down the Drain, p. D72*
  The average price of water is about 16 cents for 100 gallons.

 **How much would your family spend on water each day at this price?** Encourage students to use the data they collected in Down the Drain.

**Thinking Critically**

 **Should people have to pay for water? Why do you think so?** Encourage students to support their opinions with evidence.

 **Should people who live in drier places have to pay more for their water?** Encourage students to provide reasons to support their opinions.

**Drawing Conclusions**

- **Why does water cost money?** Money pays for treating water to make it safe for drinking. It also pays for building and taking care of the pipes that carry water to houses, schools, and businesses and it pays the salaries of the people who work at water treatment and distribution plants.

 **What do you think would happen if a gallon of water cost as much as a gallon of milk?** Perhaps people might try to use less water.

## 3. Assess Understanding

Students can work in groups of three or four. Suggest that each group come up with ideas for encouraging people to use less water. Groups can then share their ideas with the rest of the class.

## Cultural Connection

**AQUEDUCTS**

**What to Do** Tell students that the ancient Romans used aqueducts to bring water from sources far away to cities and towns. The term aqueduct comes from the Latin words *aqua,* meaning "water," and *ductus,* meaning "to lead." Suggest that students read more about these early aqueducts and draw diagrams or make models to show how they were built and how they moved water.

**What's the Result?** Students will discover that in some aqueducts, gravity alone was enough to carry the water. Other aqueducts required pumps.  **How do people today move water over long distances?** They use pipes.

# A Bargain at Any Price

**Preview** *Students focus on ways to save and protect water.*

## 1. Get Ready

### Background

- Many communities are now taking water conservation seriously. In the southwestern United States, Tucson, Arizona, has taken the lead. The city requires low-flow faucets and toilets in all new construction and sponsors educational campaigns to inform residents of the need for conservation. And if education doesn't do the trick, there are stiff fines for water wasters, and water cops to hand out the tickets. Tucson now has one of the lowest urban rates of home water use in the Southwest, 104 gallons per person daily.

### Discussion Starter

- **How much water do you think you use each day?** Encourage students to refer to the information they gathered in Down the Drain.

- **Do you ever waste water? How?** Students might say that they let the water run when they brush their teeth or get a cold drink.

# A Bargain at Any Price

Water is a bargain in this country. A bargain is an item that is sold at a low price. Maybe that's why some people use a lot of water.

### Water Use, Water Waste

In the United States, each person uses an average of 290 L (75 gal) of water a day. A family of four uses about 1,160 L (300 gal) of water a day. Recall the activity that you did on page D72. How many gallons of water does your family use every day?

Because there seems to be plenty of water in many places, most people don't realize how much water they use or how much they waste. How are the people in the drawing below wasting water? Now read the list on the next page to see some ways to conserve, or save, water.

**In what ways can you see water being wasted?** ▼

## Investigate Further

 **Integrating the Sciences**

**EARTH SCIENCE** **What to Do** Let students use the map of annual average precipitation to find out how abundant precipitation is where they live.

**What's the Result?** **What is the average yearly precipitation in your area?**  **How does the average yearly precipitation affect your water supply?** Generally, the greater the average annual precipitation, the greater the water supply.

Have students use the CD-ROM Grapher to make a graph of the precipitation data.

**D 76**    **CHAPTER 3**

## How to Save Water

- Instead of running a faucet to get water cold, put a jug of water in the refrigerator.
- Turn off faucets. Get an adult to fix leaky faucets.
- If you do dishes by hand, don't let the water run.
- Don't let the water run while you are brushing your teeth.
- As you wait for running water to get hot, catch the cool water in a bucket or pail and use it for watering plants.
- Take a brief shower (less than five minutes long) instead of a bath. If you take a bath, don't fill the tub all the way.
- Wash a car with a bucket of soapy water first. Then turn on the hose to rinse the car.
- Have an adult help you fill a plastic jug with water and put it into the tank behind your toilet. Every time you flush, you will save the amount of water that's in the jug.
- If you have a dishwasher and washing machine, wash only full loads.
- Water lawns and gardens at dusk or early in the morning to stop too much water from evaporating.

D77

## Science, Technology & Society

**SOLUTIONS** **What to Do** Tell students that in Great Britain, scientists have made special robots that can tell how clean the water in a river is. The robots take measurements that tell whether or not pollutants, such as fertilizers, are making their way into the rivers. If the scientists find proof of such pollution, they can use the robots' findings as evidence in court to convict the polluters.

**What's the Result?** Invite students to come up with their own high-tech solutions to stopping water pollution. Students can share their ideas with the class.

## 2. Guide the Discussion

*Choose from the following strategies to facilitate discussion.*

### Connecting to the Activities

- ***Down the Drain, p. D72***
 **How does your family's water use compare to the average family's water use? Why do you think your family uses more (or less)?** Encourage students to refer to their data and to consider factors such as family size and water use habits.

### Responding to Individual Needs

**Students Acquiring English** Let students make a poster showing ways to save water. Have a student proficient in English label the poster in English.

### Drawing Conclusions

- **Why do people waste water?** Possible answers: They think there is plenty of water. Water doesn't cost very much. They don't know they need to save water.
- **Why should people who live in areas with lots of water resources save and protect water?** There is only a limited supply of water on Earth and it is all connected through the water cycle.

### Making Judgments

**Should places rich in water be able to sell water to places where water is scarce?** Students should support their views with reasons and evidence.

### Thinking Critically

**Why should a leaky faucet be fixed?** Wasting water costs money and may contribute to a future water shortage.

### Drawing Conclusions

**Why shouldn't you dump chemicals down the drain or on the ground?** Because they can enter the water supply through drains or groundwater.

## 3. Assess Understanding

In groups of three or four, students should come up with ideas for the school to reduce its water use. Which ideas would save the most water? Which would be easiest to carry out? Have groups present their best ideas to the class.

## Critical Thinking Skills
**Synthesizing, Evaluating, Expressing Ideas, Solving Problems**

**1.** Students should describe ways to use water in the most conservative manner.

**2.** Answers could include fixing leaky faucets, putting plastic jugs of water in toilets, not letting the water run.

**Challenge** Encourage students to find out about other water-saving devices, such as low-flow toilets and shower heads. How much water do they save? Your local water company or plumbing supply stores may be good sources of information.

## Following Up

**Baseline Assessment** Show students their original list of water-saving ideas. Ask if they want to add any ideas now. Ask which ideas they think would be most effective.

**Reteaching** Use a simple model to demonstrate what happens when water is polluted or wasted. Show students a cup of clean water representing the water supply. Ask how it can become polluted. As students give examples, pour some of the water into another cup to which you add pollutants, such as soil, vinegar, and cooking oil. Ask how people waste water. As students give examples, spill a little of the water from the cup onto paper towels to simulate the wasted water. If people did not pollute or waste water, how much would there be in the water supply?

 Use *Science Notebook* p. 204.

**Investigation Review ▶**
Use Investigation Review page 96 in the *Assessment Guide*.

---

You've seen many ways that people waste water. You're probably most familiar with one way—not repairing leaking faucets. In the activity on page D73, you made a model of a dripping faucet. If the water that leaked filled a coffee cup in ten minutes, then 12,464 L (3,280 gal) would be wasted in a year!

**Dumping Down the Drain**

Leaks are not the only way that water is wasted. People also waste water when they pollute. The list below shows some ways you and your family can help protect water supplies from pollution. Share with others what you've learned about saving and protecting water.

### Keeping Water Safe

- Cleaners such as ammonia go down the drain and can poison the water supply. Vinegar often works just as well as ammonia for cleaning, and it isn't harmful.
- Don't dump the following things down the drain or on the ground: motor oil, medicines, paint thinner, paint, glues, spot removers, furniture polish, and antifreeze.
- Find out where your family can take used motor oil. In some communities, auto parts stores, service stations, or recycling centers will take used motor oil.
- Find out when your community collects harmful wastes.

--- INVESTIGATION 3 ---

**1.** Imagine there is a very severe water shortage. You are told you can use only 2 gal of water each day. Write a story about how you would live.

**2.** Suppose that you were in charge of saving and protecting water in your school. What kinds of things might you tell everybody to do?

D78

---

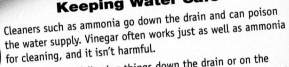

## Performance
### Group Presentation
Suggest that groups of students prepare presentations on how to save and protect water. They can make presentations to other classes in school.

Investigation Review
How Can We Save and Protect Water?

Name _____ Date _____

**1.** Put an X over the drawings that show water being wasted.

brushing teeth | washing a full load | taking a 5-minute shower | washing a car

**2.** Use the activities listed in the box to complete the chart.

| running the faucet to get cold water<br>taking a long shower<br>taking a bath when the tub is only<br>partly filled | fixing a leaky faucet<br>watering the lawn at noon<br>doing full loads of laundry |
|---|---|

| Conserving Water | Wasting Water |
|---|---|
| taking a bath with the tub only partly filled, fixing a leaky faucet, doing full loads of laundry | running the faucet to get cold water, taking a long shower, watering the lawn at noon |

First find out how water is used in order to determine where it is being wasted. For example, record the number and length of showers taken each day, how many full and partial loads of wash are done per week, and how many leaky faucets there are.

**Process Skills**
*Collecting and Recording Data*
If a friend asked you to find a way to reduce her family's water bill, what is the first thing you would do? Write your answer on a separate sheet of paper.

## Assessment

# REFLECT & EVALUATE

## WORD POWER

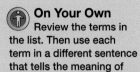

acid rain
current
polluted
tides

 **On Your Own**
Review the terms in the list. Then use each term in a different sentence that tells the meaning of the term.

**With a Partner**
Write a clue for each term in the list. Then challenge your partner to write the correct term for each clue.

**BUILD YOUR PORTFOLIO**

Think of things you can do to reduce water pollution. Then make a poster to encourage others to reduce water pollution.

### Analyze Information

Study the drawing. Then use the drawing to explain in your own words what will happen the next time it rains.

### Assess Performance

Design and carry out an activity to find out how much water you can save by not running the water the entire time you're brushing your teeth. Compare your results with those of others.

### Problem Solving

**1.** You're cleaning out the basement. Explain why you shouldn't pour old paint and paint thinners down the drain. What is the best way to get rid of these materials?

**2.** Water pollution is not a local problem, it's a global problem. Explain what this means.

**3.** A water meter doesn't run if water isn't being used. If no one in your home is using water and the water meter is running, what could this mean?

**D79**

## Chapter Test  pp. 97–98 in the Assessment Guide

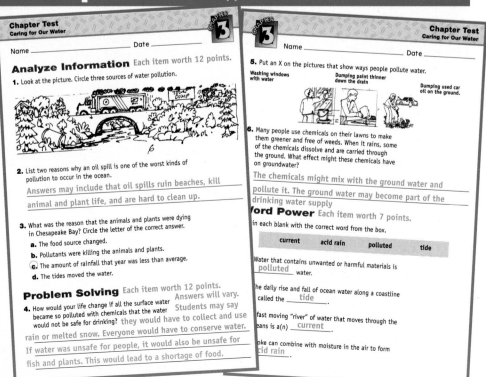

# REFLECT & EVALUATE

## Word Power

**On Your Own** Students' sentences should reflect an understanding of the terms.

**With a Partner** Partners should carefully examine any "mistakes," as the clue-writer might have misunderstood the term and expect a different answer.

## Analyze Information

Rainwater might mix with harmful substances in the dump and carry these substances into the river. They may pollute the water supply.

## Assess Performance

Evaluation could be based on the students' ability to gather accurate data, complete calculations, and chart their findings. They might begin by measuring how much water comes out of the faucet if they allow the water to run while brushing.

## Problem Solving

**1.** Substances that are poured down the drain can be carried by sewers into the water supply. Instead, you should save them until your community collects them.

**2.** Strong ocean currents and tides can carry pollution many miles away from its source. Air pollution produced in one country can cause acid rain in another country.

**3.** A faucet or toilet may be leaking and wasting water.

Use *Science Notebook* pp. 205–206.

**BUILD YOUR PORTFOLIO**

Suggest that students use their posters to educate others about the large amounts of water that can be lost through tiny drips and leaks. Display the completed posters where all students might see them.

# INVESTIGATE FURTHER!

## UNIT PROJECT:
## The Big Event

Students can begin their final preparations for the presentation of their Waterville model by deciding on a guest list and then designing and making special invitations. On the day before the event, have students work in groups to prepare the classroom. For example, groups can set up the display of the Waterville model, make a welcoming sign, prepare a refreshments table, and make copies of the calendars to be distributed to interested visitors. Assign each group a task for the presentation of Waterville. For more information on the Big Event, see Wrapping Up the Project p. D1l. For assessment use Unit Project Scoring Rubric Master D7 (TRB p. 70).

 Have students use *Science Notebook* p. 207.

## Experiment

Before students begin work on their experiments, have them develop plans to aid in setting up their terrariums and recording their observations. Allow time for students to share their long-term projects with the class.

## Take Action

In addition to posters, invite students to create advertisements and commercials promoting ways for people to take care of Earth's water. Students might share their ads with the local newspaper and commercials with a local radio station.

 ## INVESTIGATE FURTHER!

**Throughout this unit** you've investigated questions related to Earth's water. How will you use what you've learned, and share that information with others? Here are some ideas.

### Hold a Big Event
#### to Share Your Unit Project

Display your model of Waterville. Invite other classes and your family to visit your classroom to see your Waterville model and to learn about where fresh water sources are found, how water is treated and distributed to buildings, and how water can be saved and protected from pollution. Distribute your "Conserve and Care" calendars.

### Experiment

Take one of the activities in this unit a bit further. You might make a model of a water cycle by setting up a terrarium in an airtight jar or aquarium. Add soil, some plants, and a little water. Then place the terrarium in the Sun. Observe and record what happens. Or you might experiment with other materials to make a better water filter. Talk with your teacher before you carry out your plan.

### Take Action

You've learned ways that people can avoid polluting rivers. You've also learned ways that your family can save and protect water supplies. Use some of these ideas to make posters. Hang your posters in school, at home, or around your neighborhood. The posters should remind people to take care of Earth's water.

**D80**

## Home-School Connection

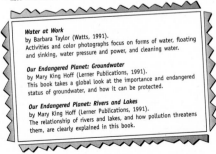

**Closing Letter**

### Dear Family,

We hope you and your student have enjoyed finding out about Earth's water. Would you like to learn more about water, how we use it, and how we can protect it from unwise use and pollutants?

- Visit a lake, river, ocean, or other body of water near your home. Look for litter, dead fish, or other signs of pollution. How might this pollution be stopped?
- In an atlas, encyclopedia, or other reference source, locate major cities around the world. How many are situated near a large body of water?
- Today, most Americans get water by turning on the faucet. Find out where and how early Native Americans or pioneers in your area got water.
- Read all about it! These books can help you learn more about Earth's water.

*Water at Work*
by Barbara Taylor (Watts, 1991).
Activities and color photographs focus on forms of water, floating and sinking, water pressure and power, and cleaning water.

*Our Endangered Planet: Groundwater*
by Mary King Hoff (Lerner Publications, 1991).
This book takes a global look at the importance and endangered status of groundwater, and how it can be protected.

*Our Endangered Planet: Rivers and Lakes*
by Mary King Hoff (Lerner Publications, 1991).
The relationship of rivers and lakes, and how pollution threatens them, are clearly explained in this book.

The Closing Letter at the end of this unit suggests additional water activities family members can do at home as well as books students and their families can read together. Distribute the Closing Letter (TRB p. 19) to students at the end of this unit.

**dissolve** (di zälv´) To mix or cause to mix one material, usually a solid, in another material, often a liquid, so that both materials separate into tiny particles that can't be seen. (D44) Sugar *dissolves* rapidly in hot water.

**distilled water** (di stild´ wôt´ər) Water that does not contain minerals, chemicals, or air. (D44) *Distilled water* is pure water.

**egg** (eg) The first stage in the life cycle of almost all animals. (A14) Birds hatch from *eggs* outside the mother bird's body.

**embryo** (em´brē ō) An animal or plant in the earliest stages of its development. (A15, A41) A plant *embryo* is the tiny plant that is found inside a seed.

**energy** (en´ər jē) The ability to move something or cause a change in matter. (C11) A car uses *energy* from gasoline to run.

**energy of motion** (en´ər jē uv mō´shən) The energy that moving matter has. (C11) Sliding downhill on a sled, tossing a basketball into the air, and flying a kite in the wind are examples of *energy of motion*.

**environment** (en vī´rən mənt) All the surrounding living and non-living things that affect a living thing. (E10) A drop of water, a rotting log, a desert, the ocean, and a rain forest are examples of different *environments*.

**enzymes** (en´zīmz) Chemicals in the body, some of which help speed up the process of digestion. (F59) Digestive *enzymes* in the stomach help the breakdown of food in the body.

**equator** (ē kwā´tər) An imaginary line that circles Earth halfway between the two poles. (B64) If you live near the *equator*, you live in a hot climate because your region receives direct sunlight year-round.

**esophagus** (i säf´ə gəs) The muscular tube that connects the mouth to the stomach. (F47) After you swallow food, it travels through the *esophagus* to the stomach.

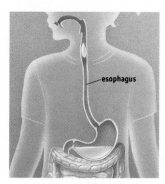

esophagus

**evaporate** (ē vap´ə rāt) To change form from a liquid to a gas. (C42, D15) On a warm dry day, water puddles on the sidewalk *evaporate* quickly.

**extinction** (ek stiŋk´shən) The permanent disappearance of all living things of a certain kind. (E31) The dinosaurs' *extinction* is a mystery that many scientists are working to solve.

**fats** (fats) High-energy nutrients that are oily or greasy. (F11) Cheeses, meats, nuts, and butter are foods that are usually high in *fats*.

**fiber** (fī´bər) Strands of plant material that are indigestible. (F61) Although *fiber* can't be digested, it aids in the process of digestion.

**flare** (fler) A bright area on the surface of the Sun caused by a solar storm. (B27) A solar *flare* is hotter than surrounding areas of the Sun and so is brighter.

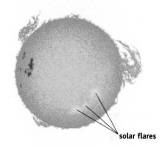

solar flares

**food chain** (fōōd chān) The path that energy takes through a community as one living thing *eats* another. (E26) The first link in a *food chain* is usually a plant.

**food web** (fōōd web) Two or more overlapping food chains. (E28) A *food web* connects animals through the plants and animals that they eat.

**fossil fuel** (fäs'əl fyōō'əl) A fuel formed over time from the remains of plants or animals. (C50) *Fossil fuels* such as oil, coal, and natural gas are found underground.

**freeze** (frēz) To change form from a liquid to a solid. (C43) The loss of heat causes a liquid to *freeze*.

**friction** (frik'shən) A force that keeps two objects from moving past one another easily. (C29) *Friction* causes your hands to get warm when you rub them together.

**fruit** (frōōt) The part of a flower that forms around a seed. (A47) Cucumbers, tomatoes, oranges, peaches, and pears are *fruits*.

**fuel** (fyōō'əl) A material that can be used for energy. (C50) Wood is a *fuel* used in many countries.

─────  G ─────

**gas** (gas) A state of matter that has no definite shape and does not take up a definite amount of space. (D14) A *gas* spreads out evenly to fill whatever space it is in.

**germ** (jʉrm) A tiny organism that can cause disease. (D49) Chlorine kills some of the *germs* in water.

**germinate** (jʉr'mə nāt) To sprout and begin to develop into a seedling. (A42) Most kinds of seeds need moisture, air, and warmth to *germinate*.

**gravity** (grav'i tē) A force that pulls two or more objects toward each other. (B22, D36) To fly into space, a rocket must overcome Earth's *gravity*.

**ground water** (ground wôt'ər) The water found beneath Earth's surface. (D27) In some areas, *ground water* fills the small spaces that are between underground rocks, soil, and sand.

─────  H ─────

**hard water** (härd wôt'ər) Water in which large amounts of minerals are dissolved. (D44) The minerals in *hard water* can stain clothing and give water an unpleasant taste.

**healthful diet** (helth'fəl dī'ət) A diet made up of a variety of foods that supply all necessary nutrients. (F18) A *healthful diet* is one that is high in fruits, vegetables, and cereals and low in fats and sweets.

**heat** (hēt) The energy of moving particles of matter. (C12) Adding *heat* to matter causes its particles to move faster.

**herbivore** (hʉr'bə vôr) An animal that eats only plants. (E18) Cows, butterflies, mice, and rabbits are *herbivores*.

**hibernation** (hī bər nā'shən) A deep sleep that helps some animals survive the winter. (E77) An animal that is in *hibernation* breathes more slowly, has a slower heartbeat, and has a lower body temperature.

─────  I ─────

**incomplete metamorphosis** (in kəm plēt' met ə môr'fə sis) The three-stage life cycle of some insects. (A26) A life cycle that goes from egg to nymph to adult is described as an *incomplete metamorphosis*.

H24

H25

**insulator** (in'sə lā tər) A poor conductor of heat or electricity. (C36) Air that is trapped in the small spaces between fibers of clothing acts as an *insulator*.

**junk food** (juŋk fōōd) A food low in nutrients and high in fat, sugar, or salt. (F30) Candy, potato chips, and soda are *junk foods*.

**large intestine** (lärj in tes'tən) The digestive organ that stores waste and absorbs water from it. (F61) The major job of the *large intestine* is to absorb water from wastes and return it to the bloodstream.

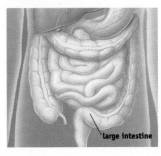

large intestine

**larva** (lär'və) The second stage in the life cycle of an insect that undergoes complete metamorphosis. (A25) A butterfly *larva* is called a caterpillar.

**life cycle** (līf sī'kəl) The series of changes that occur during the lifetime of a living thing. (A9) An insect goes through three or four stages in its *life cycle*.

**liquid** (lik'wid) A state of matter that has no definite shape but takes up a definite amount of space. (D14) At room temperature, water is a *liquid*.

**lunar eclipse** (lōō'nər i klips') The darkening of the Moon when it moves into Earth's shadow. (B78) During a *lunar eclipse*, Earth blocks the Sun's light from reaching the Moon directly.

H26

**matter** (mat'ər) Anything that has mass and takes up space. (C11) Every living and nonliving thing around you is made of *matter*.

**melt** (melt) To change form from a solid to a liquid. (C42) Ice *melts* at 0°C (32°F) or warmer.

**meteorite** (mēt'ē ər īt) A chunk of rock or metal that has fallen from space. (B11) A *meteorite* may be as small as a grain of sand or as large as a house.

**migrate** (mī'grāt) To move to another region as the seasons change. (E76) Many northern birds and butterflies *migrate* south during the winter.

**minerals** (min'ər əlz) Chemicals that can be important nutrients. (F13) Calcium is a *mineral* found in milk and cheese.

**natural resource** (nach'ər əl rē'sôrs) A material found in or on Earth that people use. (D10) *Natural resources* include water, minerals, oil, plants, and animals.

**nutrient** (nōō'trē ənt) Any substance used by living things for energy, growth, repair, or other life processes. (E43, F10) Proteins, carbohydrates, and fats are *nutrients* found in food.

**nymph** (nimf) The second stage in the life cycle of an insect undergoing incomplete metamorphosis. (A26) A grasshopper *nymph* looks similar to a small adult.

**omnivore** (äm'ni vôr) An animal that eats both plants and animals. (E18) Because bears will eat both berries and fish, bears are classified as *omnivores*.

**orbit** (ôr'bit) The path a planet, moon, or other object takes around another. (B47) The Moon is seen in different phases as it moves through its *orbit* around Earth.

orbit

H27

**palate** (pal′ət) The roof of the mouth. (F45) During the first part of digestion, the tongue mashes food against the *palate*.

**parasite** (par′ə sīt) A living thing that, at some point in its life, lives on or in another living thing. (E54) Fleas and lice are *parasites*.

**petal** (pet′′l) The brightly colored part of a flower that helps attract birds, bees, and other insects to the flower. (A46) A *petal* is one of the three main parts of a flower.

**phase** (fāz) Any stage in the series of changes in the apparent shape of the Moon. (B53) The Moon's shape appears to change with each *phase*.

**pistil** (pis′til) The central part in a flower that produces the seed. (A45) For seeds to form in a plant, the pollen must travel to the *pistil*.

**planet** (plan′it) Any large body that orbits a star and does not produce light of its own. (B47) Earth is a *planet*.

**plaque** (plak) The coating produced by bacteria on uncleaned teeth. (F51) *Plaque* is caused by bacteria in the mouth.

**pollen** (päl′ən) The powdery grains in a flower; they must be carried from a stamen to a pistil in order for seeds to form. (A46) Bees move *pollen* from one flower to another.

**pollination** (päl ə nā′shən) The process by which pollen reaches a pistil. (A46) After *pollination*, a flower can produce seeds.

**polluted** (pə lōōt′əd) Containing unwanted or harmful material. (D58) Breathing *polluted* air can be harmful to your lungs.

**precipitation** (prē sip ə tā′shən) The liquid or solid forms of water that fall to Earth. (D16) Rain, sleet, hail, and snow are different kinds of *precipitation*.

**predator** (pred′ə tər) An animal that hunts other animals for food. (E27) Hawks, cougars, and sharks are *predators*.

**prey** (prā) An animal hunted for food by another animal. (E27) Rabbits, mice, small fish, and insects are often *prey* for other, larger animals.

**producer** (prō dōōs′ər) A living thing that can make its own food. (E16) Plants, such as trees and grass, are *producers*.

**prominence** (präm′ə nəns) A huge loop of gas that appears on the edge of the Sun. (B27) *Prominences* are caused by magnetic storms on the Sun.

**proteins** (prō′tēnz) Nutrients used by the body for growth and repair. (F12) *Proteins* are found in foods such as meats, beans, nuts, and dairy products.

**pupa** (pyōō′pə) The third stage in the life cycle of an insect undergoing complete metamorphosis. (A25) As a *pupa*, an insect is enclosed in a cocoon, or case.

**radiation** (rā dē ā′shən) The movement of heat energy in the form of waves. (C37) Heat from a campfire reaches you through *radiation*.

**reservoir** (rez′ər vwär) The body of water that is stored behind a dam. (D27) A *reservoir* stores fresh water for a town or city.

**revolve** (ri välv′) To move in a circle or orbit. (B47) Earth *revolves* around the Sun.

**rotation** (rō tā′shən) Turning around an axis. (B38) Earth takes 24 hours to complete one *rotation*.

**saliva** (sə lī′və) The watery liquid, secreted into the mouth, that aids in chewing, swallowing, and digesting. (F46) *Saliva* moistens food, making it easier to swallow the food.

**salivary glands** (sal′ə ver ē glandz) Small organs that make saliva. (F46) The *salivary glands* are found under the jaw, under the tongue, and next to the ears.

**scale** (skāl) A cone's woody part on which seeds grow. (A51, A53) A pine cone's *scales* protect its seeds.

**season** (sē′zən) Any of the four parts of the year. (B65) The four *seasons* are spring, summer, fall, and winter.

**seed coat** (sēd kōt) The part of a seed that protects the plant embryo. (A41) The *seed coat* of a coconut is hard, thick, and brown.

**seedling** (sēd′liŋ) The new plant that develops from an embryo and has roots, a stem, and leaves. (A43) A tomato *seedling* can be started indoors in early spring and planted outside in May.

**small intestine** (smôl in tes′tən) The long, coiled organ in which most digestion takes place. (F60) Nutrients in food are absorbed into the bloodstream from the *small intestine*.

**soft water** (sôft wôt′ər) Water in which few minerals are dissolved. (D44) Minerals can be removed from water to make *soft water*.

**solar eclipse** (sō′lər i klips′) The blocking of light from the Sun when the Moon moves between it and Earth. (B77) During a *solar eclipse*, the Sun's light is blocked by the Moon.

**solar energy** (sō′lər en′ər jē) Energy produced by the Sun. (C20) *Solar energy* can be used to produce electricity.

**solar system** (sō′lər sis′təm) The Sun and all the planets and other objects that orbit it. (B47) Earth is one of nine planets in the *solar system*.

**solid** (säl′id) A state of matter that has a definite shape and takes up a definite amount of space. (D14) A rock, a piece of ice, and a chair are all examples of *solids*.

**species** (spē′shēz) A group of living things that can produce young by mating with one another. (A10) The lion *species* cannot produce young of the gorilla *species*.

**stamen** (stā′mən) The part of a flower that produces pollen, which is needed to form seeds. (A45) *Stamens* are often long and have a fuzzy end.

**star** (stär) A ball of very hot gases that gives off light and other kinds of energy. (B27) The Sun is a *star*.

**stomach** (stum′ək) A muscular sac that stores food and helps in digestion. (F59) The *stomach* squeezes and churns food into a souplike mixture.

**stored energy** (stôrd en′ər jē) Energy that can cause matter to move or change. (C11) Fuels have *stored energy* from the Sun.

**sunspot** (sun′spöt) A dark area on the surface of the Sun, caused by a solar storm. (B27) A *sunspot* appears darker because it is cooler than surrounding areas of the Sun.

**surface water** (sur′fis wôt′ər) Fresh water in lakes, streams, and rivers. (D26) People often pipe *surface water* to nearby cities and towns.

**telescope** (tel′ə skōp) An instrument that makes distant objects appear nearer and larger. (B14) A *telescope* is used to study stars and other planets.

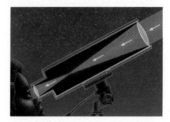

**temperature** (tem′pər ə chər) How hot or cold something is. (C28) *Temperature* is measured with a thermometer.

**tide** (tīd) The rise and fall of the ocean surface, mostly caused by the pull of the Moon's gravity. (D68) Along coasts, there are two high *tides* and two low *tides* during each day.

**H30**

**H31**

**vitamins** (vīt'ə minz) Chemicals, found in foods, that are important nutrients. (F13) *Vitamins* do not supply energy, but they are important to many body processes.

**water** (wôt'ər) A chemical, formed from hydrogen and oxygen, that is essential to life. (F12) *Water* is one of the most important nutrients.

**water cycle** (wôt'ər sī'kəl) The path that water follows from Earth to air and back again. (D16) In the *water cycle*, water evaporates from lakes and oceans into the air, and then condenses and falls back to Earth as rain or snow.

**water pressure** (wôt'ər presh'ər) The pushing of water on a surface. (D36) The deeper the water, the greater the *water pressure* becomes.

**water vapor** (wôt'ər vā'pər) Water that is a gas. (D15) Steam, which is invisible, is a form of *water vapor.*

**H32**

# INDEX

## A

Acid
in mouth, F51
in stomach, F59
Acid rain, D56–D57*, D59, D62
Adaptation, A42, A60, A62, E36, E38*, E40. See also Behavior of animals; Camouflage; Protection.
in animals, E40–E43, E54–E55
to environment, E70*, E72, E74–E75
in plants, A60–A62, E43
Adult, A9, A24–A27
Air, A43, A54, B12–B13, C18, C33*, C37–C38, D10, D15, D49, F62
Alaska
midnight sun, B71
Animals, A6–A7*, A8–A9, A10–A11, A42, A48, A55, B28, D69, D70
baby animals, A10, A18, A28–A29*
claws, E40
eggs, A14, A16, A18
fangs, E40
growth and change, A20–A21*
life cycle, A12–A13*
senses, E40
tongues, E40, E41, E44–E45
use of tools, E42–E43
Annuals (flowers), A48
Aquifer, D27–D28, D61
Ogalalla Aquifer, D61
Arctic tern, E76
Aryabhata I, B48
Astronaut, B21, B23, B30
Aldrin, Buzz, B23
Armstrong, Neil, B23

## B

Astronomer, B14, B29
Atmosphere, B12
on Earth, B12
on Moon, B13
Axis, B38–B39, B65

Bacteria, D49, D51, E13, F34–F35, F36–F37, F51, F53, F62. See also Germs.
needs of, E13
Beavers, E64–E65
Beetles, E73
Behavior of animals, E42, E52–E54
as adaptation, E42
as protection, E52–E54
stalking of prey, E43
**Benchmarks and Standards**
*See Project 2061 Benchmarks and National Science Education Standards*
Binoculars, B15
Birds, A8, A42, A45, A47, A48, A55, A62, C38, E38–E39*, E55, E67, E76
beaks (bills), E38–E39*, E41–E42
feathers, C38
water birds, E64
Birdseye, Clarence, F35
Blood, F12
Bloodstream, F44, F60
Blood vessels, F61
Body, F10, F12, F18, F44, F56
growth, F10, F12, F18, F31
repair, F10, F12, F18
Bog, E66
Bones, F13
Breathing, F12
Buffaloes (bison), E68–E69
Wood Buffalo Park, E69

## C

Bulb (plant), A41, A43
Burning (a way of changing matter), C44
Bush, A54
Butterfly, A25

Cactus, A60, E75
Calendars, B67–B69
of Caesar, B68–B69
Chinese, B68
Greenwich, England, B69
Mayan, B67
Roman, B68–B69
Calories, F26–F27*, F28, F30
Camouflage, E45
in animals, E50
in chameleons, E45
in insects, E48–E49*
Canning (to keep food fresh), F35
Car, C4, C11, C12, C18
Carbohydrates, F10–F11, F13, F18–F20, F28–F29, F59. See also Starches; Sugar.
Carbon dioxide, A16
**Careers**
Animal breeder, C22
Biologist, A4
Biotechnologist, A36
Cultural anthropologist, B58
Energy surveyor, C46
Environmental scientist, D54
Firefighter, D30
Folk song musician, B32
Food editor, F4
Pedodontist, F40
Planetary geologist, B4
Science writer, D4
Solar energy systems designer, C4
Teacher, E4
Wildlife photographer, E60

*Activity
Blue entries indicate Teaching Guide material.

*Activity
Blue entries indicate Teaching Guide material.

D50, D52, D60

Land, D6–D7*, D9, E66

Large intestine. See Intestines: large.

Larva, A24–A25, A31

Laser
  as dental tool, F52–F53

Leaf, A41, A42, A52, A60, E78

Leeuwenhoek, Anton van, D50

Life cycle, A6–A7*, A9, A12–A13*, A14, A19, A24, A61
  of conifer, A53–A54
  of flowering plant, A48–A49
  four-stage, A25
  of insects, A24
  of mealworm beetle, A20–A21*, A26
  three-stage, A26
  of tree, A54

Life span, A10

Light, A58–A59*, A60, C13
  laser, F52

Light bulb, C19, F52

Lightning, C12

Light waves, C13

Lignite, C59

Liquid, C27–C28, C33*, C36, C42–C43, D14, D17, D37

Liver, F60

Living things, E10–E13, E60, E62–E63*, E67, E70–E71*

Lunar eclipse, B72–B73*, B78

Lungs, F12, F46

Machines, C12

Maize, A40

Mars, B4

Marsh, E66–E67

Mass, B22, C11
  of Earth, B22
  of Moon, B22

Mate, A10, A16, A25

Matter, C11, C13, C27–C29, C37, D14
  as a liquid, C27–C28, C33*, C36, C42–C43, D14, D17, D37
  changes in, C44
  contracting of, C44

expanding of, C44
  as a gas, C27–C28, C33*, C36, C42–C43, D14, D17
  movement of, C27–C29, C35–C37, C42–C44
  particles in, C27–C29, C32*, C35–C37, C42–C44
  shape of, C27, D14
  as a solid, C27–C28, C32*, C33*, C35–C36, C42–C43, D14, D17
  space taken up by, C27–C28, D14

Meadow, E65

Medicines, from nature, E56–E58

Melting, C42

Metamorphosis
  complete, A25
  incomplete, A26

Meteor, B4

Meteorite, B11–B12

Microscope, B12, D50

Microwave oven, C27

Microwaves, C29

Migration, E76, E78

Minerals (in diet), F10, F13, F14, F18–F19, F28–F29

**Misconceptions**
  A4, A36, B4, B32, B58, C4, C22, C46, D4, D30, D54, E4, E36, E60, F4, F40

Moisture, A42, A43, A50–A51*, A53, A54, E72–E74

Molds, E15

Moon, B4, B6–B7*, B8–B9*, B10–B11, B14, B16–B17, B18–B19*, B20, B52–B55, D68
  air, B13
  atmosphere, B13
  craters, B8–B9*, B11–B12
  effects on Earth, B56
  gravity, B23, B56
  mass, B22
  mountains, B11
  new moon, B54
  phases, B50–B51*, B53
  plains, B11
  revolution, B52–B53
  rock as part of, B10–B11, B22

Sea of Tranquillity, B11
  size, B6–B7*
  sky of, B13
  soil as part of, B10, B16, B23
  temperature, B13
  valleys, B11
  water, B13

Motion, C8–C9*

Mucus, F59

**Multi-Age Classroom**
  A8, B10, B11, B53, B65, C11, C17, C27, D15, D16, D36, D37, D50, D57, D62, D66, D67, D70, D73, D74, E17, E22, E39, E41, F52

**Multi-Age Strategies**
  A6, A44, A58, B8, B18, B20, B44, B50, B60, C14, C48, C53, D8, D22, D34, D56, D66, E6, E15, E24, E62, E70, F16, F26, F49

Muscles, F12, F45, F47, F58–F62

**National Science Education Standards**
  A1c, B1c, C1c, D1c, E1c, F1c

Natural resources, D10, D61

Nectar, A47

Needles (of plants), A52

Neighborhood, E62–E63*

Night, E74, E76

North Pole, B14, B38, B40

North Star, B40. See also Constellations: Polaris.

Northern Hemisphere, B65

Northern lights, B29

Nose, F42–F43*, F44
  nasal cavity, F46
  nasal passages, F44

Nutrients, E43, F10, F14–F15, F16–F17*, F18, F30–F31, F40, F60–F61

Nutrition information, F28

Nymph, A23*, A26–A27

*Activity
Blue entries indicate Teaching Guide material.